MANAGERIAL ACCOUNTING PRINCIPLES WORKBOOK
V3.0

Lead Author
Dr. Jeffrey L. Hillard, DM, CMA, CPA
Notre Dame of Maryland University

Collaborating Authors
John Wiley, BS, M. Ed.
Baltimore City Community College

Dr. Anthony A. Atkinson, PhD, FCMA, FCPA
Wilfrid Laurier University

Contributors and Reviewers

Sherry Davidson, BBA, CPA,CMA, EMBA
Georgian College

Dr. Cathy Duffy, BSc, MS, EdD
Champlain College

Suryakant Desai, EdD, CPA, CFP
Cedar Valley College

Anne Neal, BA, CPA, CMA, MAc
Algonquin College

Authors of Managerial Accounting Principles, Second Edition © 2011

Neville Joffe

Dr. Anthony Atkinson, PhD, FCMA, FCPA
Wilfrid Laurier University

Textbook ISBN: 978-1-926751-94-8
Workbook ISBN: 978-1-926751-95-5

Managerial Accounting Principles, V3.0
Authors: Jeff Hillard/John Wiley/Anthony Atkinson
Publisher: AME Learning Inc.
Project Manager: Lisa McManus
Content Contributors and Developmental Editors:
        Kobboon Chotruangprasert/Vicki Austin/Anne Neal
Production Editors: Graeme Gomes/Lisa McManus
Copy Editor: Lisa McManus
Indexer: Elizabeth Walker
Typesetter: Paragon Prepress Inc.
VP Product Development and Technology: Linda Zhang
Cover Design: Pixon Design
Online Course Design & Production: AME eLearning Team

4 5 Webcom 20 19

This book is written to provide accurate information on the covered topics.
It is not meant to take the place of professional advice.

For more information contact:

AME Learning Inc.
410-1220 Sheppard Avenue East
Toronto, ON, Canada M2K 2S5
Phone: 416.479.0200
Toll-free: 1.888.401.3881
E-mail: info@amelearning.com
Visit our website at: www.amelearning.com

Table of Contents

Chapter 1

AN OVERVIEW OF MANAGERIAL ACCOUNTING

LEARNING OBJECTIVES

LO 1   Define managerial accounting and explain how it differs from financial accounting

LO 2   Describe the importance of managerial accounting

LO 3   Describe the stages involved in the management process

LO 4   Define cost, cost object and cost driver

LO 5   Describe the importance of the value chain

LO 6   Explain the differences between product costs and period costs

LO 7   Calculate cost of goods manufactured and cost of goods sold

LO 8   Explain the importance of ethics related to managerial accounting

AMEENGAGE   *Access **ameengage.com** for integrated resources including tutorials, practice exercises, the digital textbook and more.*

Assessment Questions

AS-1 LO 1

What is managerial accounting?

_____

_____

AS-2 LO 1

What is financial accounting?

_____

_____

AS-3 LO 1

Briefly describe five differences between managerial and financial accounting.

_____

_____

_____

_____

AS-4 LO 3

What are the two main stages in making decisions?

_____

_____

_____

AS-5 `LO 4`

Describe the three main types of businesses.

_____

_____

_____

AS-6 `LO 4`

Provide three real world companies for each type of business.

_____

_____

_____

AS-7 `LO 2`

Provide an example of a profession or occupation that will benefit from an understanding of management accounting, and explain how it might be helpful.

_____

_____

_____

AS-8 `LO 7`

What is the purpose of a formal income statement?

_____

_____

_____

AS-9 `LO 8`

Based on the Institute of Management Accountants (IMA), briefly indicate the standards that members must comply with.

_____

_____

AS-10 `LO 8`

Why is it important for managerial accountants to follow the code of ethics?

_____

_____

AS-11 LO 5

What is the value chain within an organization?

_____

_____

AS-12 LO 5

List six phases in a manufacturing organization's value chain.

_____

_____

_____

_____

_____

_____

AS-13 LO 6

What are product costs?

_____

_____

AS-14 LO 6

What are period costs?

_____

_____

AS-15 LO 6

What are direct costs?

_____

_____

AS-16 LO 6

What are indirect costs?

_____

_____

AS-17 LO 7

What are the three forms of inventory in a manufacturing company? Discuss each.

_____

_____

_____

_____

_____

AS-18 LO 7

Discuss the flow of inventory in a manufacturing environment. Include the raw materials, WIP and finished goods accounts in your discussion.

_____

_____

_____

_____

_____

_____

AS-19 LO 7

Why is it important for a manufacturer to accurately calculate how much it costs to manufacture the goods they sell?

_____

_____

_____

_____

AS-20 LO 7

Which line item(s) on the formal income statement does cost of goods manufactured affect?

_____

_____

AS-21 LO 7

What is the difference between a perpetual inventory system and a periodic inventory system?

_____

_____

_____

AS-22 LO 3

What are the three major planning processes?

_____
_____
_____
_____
_____
_____

AS-23 LO 4

What is a cost object?

_____
_____
_____
_____
_____
_____

AS-24 LO 7

What is included in the value of cost of goods sold for a merchandising company?

_____
_____
_____
_____
_____
_____

AS-25 LO 7

How does a service company calculate the cost associated with providing their services?

_____
_____
_____
_____
_____
_____
_____

Application Questions Group A

AP-1A LO 1

Indicate whether the following statements describe financial accounting (FA) or managerial accounting (MA).

	a) Must follow Generally Accepted Accounting Principles (GAAP) or International Financial Reporting Standards (IFRS) set by professional bodies.
	b) Largely based on forecasting future sales and cash flows, calculating costs and preparing budgets.
	c) Is concerned with collecting data of historical nature.
	d) Does not require independent examination.
	e) Primarily prepared for external users such as creditors and stockholders so that they can make sound financial or investment decisions.
	f) Reports are very detailed and provide a wealth of information.

AP-2A LO 2 4

Everything Electronics operates a large store in New York. The store sells cell phones, televisions and various electronics.

As discussed at the beginning of the chapter, organizations fall into three main categories with respect to the type of business they are in. What type of business is Everything Electronics in? Why is it important for the owner of Everything Electronics to understand managerial accounting?

_____

_____

_____

_____

_____

AP-3A LO 6

Following are ABC Company's production costs for April:

Direct Materials	$90,000
Direct Labor	$30,000
Manufacturing Overhead	$5,000

Calculate the total cost that can be directly traced to specific products in the production process.

_____

_____

_____

AP-4A LO 6

Top of the Head Comb Company incurred the costs listed below during May to manufacture combs. The company uses a JIT inventory system.

Plastic resin	$3,500
Factory machine blades (replaced once each month)	500
Cost to ship to customers	600
Production supervisor's salary	2,100
Product advertising costs	1,200
Production labor	42 hours at $20 per hour

a) Calculate total product costs assuming 10,000 combs are produced.

b) What is the cost per comb?

AP-5A LO 7

Gamma Corporation compiled the following list of costs related to manufacturing for the year ended December 31, 2019:

Direct materials used in production	$450,000
Direct labor	320,000
Total manufacturing overhead	600,000

They have also provided the following information:

- The balance of work in process inventory on January 1, 2019 is equal to the balance of work in process inventory on December 31, 2019.

- Finished goods inventory had a balance of $180,000 on January 1, 2019 and a balance of $220,000 on December 31, 2019.

Required

a) Calculate the cost of goods manufactured for the year ended December 31, 2019.

_____

_____

_____

_____

b) Calculate cost of goods sold for the year and show how the cost of goods sold section would appear in a detailed income statement.

_____

_____

_____

_____

_____

AP-6A LO 8

Taylor Accountants LLP recently hired a university student for the summer. With little knowledge on accounting and lack of work experience, the student continued to perform various tasks without any supervision. These tasks include analyzing financial statements and providing recommendations to clients.

According to the IMA standards, which of the four standards did the company violate and why?

_____

_____

_____

_____

_____

AP-7A LO 8

After a meeting with M&T Accountant LLP, the CEO of Bill Jonny Corporation decided to have lunch in the cafeteria (which was located in the same building as M&T). As he was about to leave, he noticed that all of Bill Jonny Corporation's financial records were scattered on the ground. At this point, the CEO was extremely upset with M&T, since these records were meant for internal use only. Two days after the incident, Bill Jonny Corporation filed a lawsuit against its accounting firm, M&T Accountants LLP.

Which of the four IMA standards did Bill Jonny Corporation sue M&T Accountants LLP for breaching and why?

_____

_____

_____

_____

_____

AP-8A LO 7

Hoth Company is a brand new company that started operations on December 1, 2019. Hoth manufactures cold weather clothing. At the end of December, 2019, the accountant for Hoth compiled the following information.

Administrative Expense	25,000
Direct Labor	10,000
Ending Finished Goods	8,000
Ending Raw Materials	20,000
Ending Work-in-Process	7,000
Manufacturing Overhead	6,000
Raw Material Purchases	50,000
Sales Revenue	120,000
Selling Expense	30,000

Required

a) Prepare a schedule of cost of goods manufactured for December.

b) Prepare an income statement for December.

AP-9A LO 7

Lando Corporation is a retail store that sells capes. The accounting has compiled the following data for the month of July, 2019.

Administrative Expense	32,000
Beginning Merchandise Inventory	75,000
Ending Merchandise Inventory	62,000
Merchandise Purchases	110,000
Sales Revenue	230,000
Selling Expense	21,000

Prepare the income statement for the month of July.

—————————— **Application Questions Group B** ——————————

AP-1B `LO 1`

Owen's Office Supply sells office supplies, office furniture and equipment from four stores in a major metropolitan city. The accountant for Owen's Office Supply is preparing the year-end financial statements for 2019 and also creating forecasted financial statements. Indicate whether the items listed would use <u>historical</u> information or <u>forecast</u> information.

Sales for 2019	
Cost of goods sold for next year	
Budgeted income statement	
Actual income from operations	
Expected gross profit	

AP-2B `LO 4 5 6`

Signet makes costume jewelry and play jewelry for children. The company uses a number of raw materials such as plastic pellets and metal clips to make the jewelry. Most of the manufacturing process is automated by machines, but some employees are still required to load the raw materials and extract the finished product.

What type of business is Signet in? Provide examples of costs that would be included as part of the manufacturing process and classify them as direct labor, direct materials or manufacturing overhead.

_____

_____

_____

_____

AP-3B `LO 6 7`

Top Strings Inc. manufactures several wood and string instruments. In particular, it is well-known for its production of classic guitars. Assume that Top Strings uses a periodic inventory system and a physical count of inventory takes place at year end. The company accumulated the following costs and account balances for the year ended December 31, 2019 with respect to direct materials:

Balance of materials on January 1, 2019	$200,000
Balance of materials on December 31, 2019	150,000
Materials purchases during 2019	750,000

In addition, the following table shows Top Strings' remaining costs for the year:

Indirect materials	$60,000
Direct labor	300,000
Indirect labor	160,000
Utilities, factory	70,000
Utilities, office	20,000
Insurance, factory	15,000
Advertising	25,000

Required

a) Calculate the cost of direct materials used in production for the year.

_____

_____

_____

_____

b) What is the total manufacturing overhead cost for the year?

_____

_____

_____

_____

_____

_____

_____

c) Calculate total manufacturing costs.

_____

_____

_____

d) If there is no beginning work in process inventory and ending work in process inventory is $50,000, what is the cost of goods manufactured?

_____

_____

_____

_____

AP-4B LO 6

Francis Company manufactures wooden jewelry boxes. The following financial data pertains to costs incurred in one day of operations.

Costs	Amount
Supplies Used (office only)	$100
Lumber	2,500
Nails	250
Varnish	400
Paints	500
Marketing Expenses	350
Plant Supervisor's Salaries	150
Carpenters' Salaries	300
Total Cost	**$4,550**

Required

a) Determine the total dollar amount of product costs for the day.

_____

_____

b) Determine the direct costs for the day.

_____

_____

_____

_____

c) Calculate total indirect manufacturing costs for the day.

_____

_____

_____

AP-5B LO 7

The following is data pertaining to XYZ Corporation's manufacturing operation for the month of December:

	Beginning	Ending
Direct Materials	$18,000	$15,000
Work-in-Process	9,000	6,000
Finished Goods	27,000	36,000

Additional information for the month of December

Direct Materials Purchased	$42,000
Direct Labor Payroll	30,000
Factory Overhead	20,000

Calculate cost of goods manufactured and cost of goods sold.

AP-6B LO 8

Gordon & Morgan LLP (G&M) is an accounting firm. The firm compiles financial statements and also provides managerial consulting to their clients. Two days ago, Finley Company approached Gordon, the controlling partner of Finley, for managerial accounting assistance. The client has been experiencing significant losses for the past few years, and for the very first time, the board of directors of Finley Company demanded a particular set of financial reports. Finley's CEO made a personal offer to Gordon. He will pay Gordon an additional 20% if Gordon ensures the report on income to be prepared for Finley's board of directors will not present a net loss. Gordon accepted the CEO's offer.

Which of the four IMA standards did Gordon violate and why?

_____

_____

_____

_____

_____

_____

AP-7B LO 8

At year end, the accounting department of QRT Limited is required to provide a set of financial statements. For the past two years, QRT has been experiencing financial difficulties and 70% of its noncurrent assets have been used as collateral for a bank loan. To make QRT's stockholders confident about the company's operations, the accounting department decided to withhold information regarding the collateral.

According to the IMA standards, which of the four standards did the company violate and why?

_____

_____

_____

_____

_____

_____

AP-8B LO 7

Deep Water manufactures scuba masks. For the month of March 2019, Deep Water reported the following data.

Administrative Expense	37,000
Beginning Finished Goods	120,000
Beginning Raw Materials	150,000
Beginning Work-in-Process	60,000
Direct Labor	50,000
Ending Finished Goods	90,000
Ending Raw Materials	130,000
Ending Work-in-Process	45,000
Manufacturing Overhead	42,000
Raw Material Purchases	230,000
Sales Revenue	450,000
Selling Expense	48,000

Required

a) Prepare a schedule of cost of goods manufactured for March.

b) Prepare an income statement for the month of March.

AP-9B LO 7

Bender and Associates is a legal firm practicing family law. Many clients have cases that cover several months. Fees charged to clients are usually billed once a case has been settled. The accounting for the law firm has the following information at the end of August, 2019.

Administrative Expense	125,000
Beginning Work-in-Progress Billing	380,000
Ending Work-in-Progress Billing	420,000
Selling Expense	42,000
Service Revenue	780,000
Work-in-Progress Billings for the Period	520,000

Prepare an income statement for the law firm for August.

Case Study

CS-1 LO 2 3 6 7

Oscar Tame is the CEO of AnyDoppler Inc. His company manufactures ultra-thin speaker pads. Each pad has a wire that can connect to an iPod. The pad can be placed on any surface (e.g. wall, table or window) and utilizes the material properties of the surface to turn it into a speaker that transmits sound when activated. Oscar hired a plant manager, Sybil Vain, to oversee factory operations. He pays her an annual salary of $100,000. Factory rent amounts to $30,000 per year. During the year, Sybil purchased $500,000 worth of factory capital assets. There are 25 assembly line workers who work 8 hours a day, for 4 days a week, for 50 weeks a year at $30 per hour. The factory has a high-tech inventory system that is able to trace raw materials to each finished good accurately and inexpensively. During the year, the factory used $350,000 worth of raw materials to produce the speaker pads. Depreciation of the factory equipment amounted to $15,000 and factory electricity expenses amounted to $10,000. At the beginning of the year, Oscar purchased three company cars for the sales team. Each car cost the company $45,000. The depreciation on these cars amounted to $5,000 for the year. During the year, Oscar spent $400,000 on marketing campaigns. Oscar was paid $200,000 for the year and paid his receptionist $45,000 per year.

a) Calculate AnyDoppler's product and period costs. Explain your reasons for identifying costs as either product or period costs.

b) Calculate AnyDoppler's direct costs and indirect manufacturing costs. Provide explanations.

_____

_____

_____

_____

_____

_____

_____

_____

_____

_____

_____

_____

c) When Oscar was reviewing the financial statements at the end of the year, he noticed that Sybil produced 10,000 units of inventory despite the fact that he told her throughout the year that they only needed to sell 6,000 units. Now the company has 4,000 units in inventory and runs the risk of them being stolen or becoming obsolete. Why do you think Sybil over-produced inventory? Note that, at the beginning of the year, Oscar introduced a bonus compensation scheme whereby Sybil would be rewarded handsomely if she reduced manufacturing expenses. (Hint: Consider the connection among excess inventory, capitalization and allocation of product costs and how Sybil is compensated.)

_____

_____

_____

_____

_____

_____

_____

_____

_____

_____

_____

_____

_____

_____

_____

Chapter 2

JOB ORDER COSTING

LEARNING OBJECTIVES

LO **1** Describe the concept of job order costing

LO **2** Apply direct materials and direct labor to the total cost of a job

LO **3** Account for the application of manufacturing overhead to the total cost of a job

LO **4** Account for underallocated or overallocated manufacturing overhead

LO **5** Analyze inventory and gross margin

LO **6** Describe ethics related to confidentiality and risk management

AMEENGAGE™ *Access **ameengage.com** for integrated resources including tutorials, practice exercises, the digital textbook and more.*

Assessment Questions

AS-1 LO **1**

Explain the characteristics of job order costing.

_____

_____

_____

AS-2 LO **2**

Discuss the differences between the raw materials, work-in-process and finished goods accounts in job order costing.

_____

_____

_____

_____

AS-3 LO **2**

Once a job has been completed, what is the journal entry to move cost in WIP to finished goods inventory?

_____

_____

AS-4 LO **2**

Once a sale has been made, what happens to cost of goods sold and finished goods inventory?

_____

_____

AS-5 LO 1

Discuss the difference between subsidiary ledgers (subledgers) and the general ledger. Provide three examples of subledgers.

_____

_____

_____

AS-6 LO 2

What is the purpose of issuing a materials requisition form?

_____

_____

_____

AS-7 LO 2

What are labor time tickets used for? What information do they contain?

_____

_____

_____

AS-8 LO 3

What is the manufacturing overhead account and where are actual and estimated overhead costs recorded?

_____

_____

_____

_____

AS-9 LO 3

Give three examples of costs that can be included in manufacturing overhead.

_____

_____

_____

AS-10 LO 3

What is a cost allocation base? Provide two examples of allocation bases.

_____

_____

_____

AS-11 LO 3

What is the predetermined overhead rate used for and how is it calculated?

AS-12 LO 3

What are departmental overhead rates and when are they used?

AS-13 LO 3 4

Explain the difference between how actual and allocated manufacturing overhead costs are recorded in an organization's accounting system.

AS-14 LO 4

When do underallocated and overallocated overhead occur?

AS-15 LO 4

Explain the cost of goods sold approach to account for underallocated or overallocated overhead costs.

AS-16 LO 2

Under the proration method, to which accounts is under or overallocated overhead costs attributed?

_____

_____

AS-17 LO 2

What are the two methods for accounting for under or overallocated overhead costs? Which method is more commonly used and why?

_____

_____

_____

_____

_____

AS-18 LO 1

When should job order costing be used?

_____

_____

_____

_____

AS-19 LO 5

A company generates $800 of gross profit per product. A manufacturing job of 10 items was accepted and six of the products were delivered to the customer by the end of the July. The remaining four products are still WIP. How must gross profit was earned in July?

_____

_____

_____

AS-20 LO 6

Describe the purpose of internal controls as they relate to accounting and production information.

_____

_____

_____

Application Questions Group A

AP-1A LO 2

GreenApple Manufacturer Inc. produces custom apple-shaped water bottles. GreenApple has two employees, Candice and Aaron. Both Candice and Aaron are paid wages of $10/hour. Their job cards are shown below.

Labor Time Card					
GreenApple Manufacturer Inc.					
Card #: 8		Week Start:	Sept 1, 2019		
		Week End:	Sept 4, 2019		
Candice A.					
Date	**Description**	**Hours**	**Rate**	**Total**	
Sept 1	Job ID # 4	7	$10	$70	
Sept 2	Job ID # 3	7	$10	$70	
Sept 3	Job ID # 5	6	$10	$60	
Sept 4	Job ID # 4	6	$10	$60	
		Total	26		$260
		Total Direct Labor:			**$260**

Handwritten notes (left margin): Sept 1st - 7, Sept 4th - 6
Handwritten notes (right margin): } 130

Labor Time Card					
GreenApple Manufacturer Inc.					
Card #: 9		Week Start:	Sept 1, 2019		
		Week End:	Sept 4, 2019		
Aaron B.					
Date	**Description**	**Hours**	**Rate**	**Total**	
Sept 1	Job ID # 1	7	$10	$70	
Sept 2	Job ID # 1	7	$10	$70	
Sept 3	Job ID # 4	7	$10	$70	
Sept 4	Job ID # 4	7	$10	$70	
		Total	28		$280
		Total Direct Labor:			**$280**

Handwritten notes (left margin): Sept 3rd - 7, Sept 4th - 7
Handwritten notes (right margin): ↕ → 270 ; 7 140

Required

a) Calculate the cost of direct labor for Job ID #4 during the week.

_____

_____

_____

_____

_____

b) GreenApple Manufacturer also incurred $500 of indirect labor costs. On September 5, GreenApple makes an entry to transfer direct and indirect labor costs to WIP and manufacturing overhead. What is the journal entry to apply direct and indirect labor for Job ID #4?

Date	Account Title and Explanation	Debit	Credit

AP-2A LO 2 3 4

The following information was reported by Fyfe Company relating to its first year of operations. Note that Fyfe has only identified direct labor and direct materials as direct costs.

Item	Expected Cost	Actual Cost
Advertising Expenditures	$156,000	$144,000
Depreciation on Factory Equipment	540,000	570,000
Direct Labor	900,000	925,000
Direct Materials	1,200,000	1,100,000
Factory Supplies	102,000	107,000
Head Office General Expenditures	340,000	325,000
Head Office Salaries	340,000	345,000
Heating in Factory	125,000	145,000
Income Taxes	2,500,000	2,450,000
Factory Equipment Repair and Maintenance	102,000	98,000
Production Supervisor Wages	123,000	128,000
Rent for Factory	950,000	945,000
Office Supplies	124,000	129,000
Sales Expenditures	432,000	456,000
Total	$7,934,000	$7,867,000

Fyfe Company allocates manufacturing overhead using a predetermined overhead rate. Fyfe uses direct labor hours as an allocation base and incurs 36,000 direct labor hours.

Required

a)   What is the total estimated manufacturing overhead cost?

_____

_____

_____

Item	Expected Cost

b)   What is the predetermined overhead rate?

_____

_____

_____

_____

_____

_____

_____

_____

c)   If the hourly rate for direct labor is $25, what is the manufacturing overhead applied to production?

_____

_____

_____

_____

_____

_____

_____

_____

_____

_____

d)   What is the over or underallocated manufacturing overhead for this year? Assume the wage rate is still $25/hr.

_____

_____

_____

Item	Actual Cost

AP-3A LO 3 4

ABC Company makes a wide variety of gear assemblies for industrial applications. The company uses job order costing, with a predetermined overhead rate of $4.50 per machine hour. During May 2019, ABC worked on the following jobs.

	Job # 52	Job #53	Job #54
Direct Materials Used on Job	$14,910	$16,640	$7,010
Direct Labor Cost	$19,450	$13,600	$10,050
Machine Hours	1,390	1,480	830

Required

a) Calculate the amount of overhead to be allocated to each job.

_____

_____

_____

_____

b) Assume actual overhead for May was $15,410, indicate whether overhead was under or overallocated.

_____

_____

_____

AP-4A LO 3

Danny Company has expected total manufacturing overhead of $15,000,000 and has decided that the appropriate cost driver to use to allocate manufacturing overhead to jobs is machine hours. The expected machine hours are 20,000. The capacity machine hours are 24,000. The long-run average is 22,000 hours.

Calculate the manufacturing overhead rate per machine hour that would be used in each of the three approaches.

_____

_____

_____

AP-5A LO 3 4

Maggie Company allocates manufacturing overhead to jobs based on machine hours. Just before the current accounting period, Maggie estimated that total manufacturing overhead costs would amount to $1,800,000 and total machine hours would amount to 15,000. During the year, the actual manufacturing overhead was $1,850,000 and the actual number of machine hours was 16,000.

Required

a) What is the predetermined overhead rate that Maggie Company used to allocate manufacturing overhead to production?

_____

_____

b) Was manufacturing overhead over or underallocated during the year?

_____

_____

_____

AP-6A LO 3

Angus Company has organized its manufacturing operations into two departments – machining and assembly. The total allocated manufacturing overhead in the machining and assembly departments were $3,000,000 and $1,000,000 respectively. In the machining department, estimated total direct labor hours and estimated total machine hours were 3,500 and 20,000 respectively. In the assembly department, estimated total direct labor hours and estimated total machine hours were 12,500 and 2,500 respectively.

During the year, Job Q544 used 20 machine hours and 5 direct labor hours in the machining department. It also used 2 machine hours and 14 direct labor hours in the assembly department.

Required

a) Angus Company allocates manufacturing overhead to jobs using one predetermined overhead rate for the entire plant. This is based on direct labor hours as an allocation base. How much manufacturing overhead would be allocated to Job Q544?

b) Suppose Angus Company uses departmental predetermined overhead rates to allocate expected department overhead costs to jobs. In the machining department, manufacturing overhead is allocated based on machine hours. In the assembly department, direct labor hours are used as the allocation base.   What is the total manufacturing overhead that would be allocated to Job Q544?

_____

_____

_____

_____

_____

_____

_____

_____

_____

_____

_____

_____

c)   What is the journal entry to allocate the manufacturing overhead in part (b) above?

Date	Account Title and Explanation	Debit	Credit

AP-7A LO 3 4

During its first year of operations, Pepper Company had estimated total manufacturing overhead to be $2,250,000. Pepper Company used direct labor hours as an allocation base for the predetermined overhead rate. Estimated total direct labor hours for the year was 18,000 and actual total direct labor hours amounted to 20,000. The direct labor wage rate is $25/hr. Actual total manufacturing overhead was 105% of estimated allocated manufacturing overhead.

The ending balances in work-in-process, finished goods inventory, and cost of goods sold before any adjustment for over or under allocated manufacturing overhead were $500,000, $1,500,000, and $3,000,000 respectively. An analysis of the account balances concluded that actual direct labor cost was 10% of the account balance for all three accounts.

Required

a) Suppose Pepper Company has a policy of allocating any over or underallocated manufacturing overhead to cost of goods sold. Calculate the amount of over or underallocated manufacturing overhead.

When	Calculation	Result
Before		
During		
After		

b) Record the appropriate adjusting entry for part a).

Date	Account Title and Explanation	Debit	Credit

AP-8A LO 3

Horizon Company, a well-known manufacturer of high quality speed boats, provided the following information for the month of April 2019.

	Job #6	Job #7	Job #8
Direct Materials	$28,000	$24,400	$27,500
Direct Labor	24,000	23,900	22,600
Allocated Manufacturing Overhead	20,200	21,100	25,300
Total	$72,200	$69,400	$75,400

The April sales report showed that Job #6 and #8 were sold for cash amounting to $99,000 and $103,500 respectively. Job #7 is still unsold.

Record the above sale and cost of goods sold. (Do not record WIP journal entries.) Assume that Horizon Company uses a perpetual inventory system.

Date	Account Title and Explanation	Debit	Credit

AP-9A LO 5

Office Plus Furniture has just completed building 10 tables for customer Prestige Worldwide and has delivered them to the customer. The job order is #6253. Below are the financial details regarding the tables on a per unit basis.

Sales Price $750
Direct Labor $100
Direct Material $250
Manufacturing Overhead $75

Using this information, prepare a Job Order Cost and Margin Record for this job.

AP-10A LO 5

ABC Company had the following results of operation for the year ending 2019.

Products Sold	80,000
Price per Product	$10
Direct Materials Used	$200,000
Direct Labor Used	$135,000
Manufacturing Overhead	$165,000
Selling Expenses	$30,000
Administrative Expenses	$85,000

Calculate the gross profit and gross margin for the year.

Application Questions Group B

AP-1B LO 2 3

Northwest Outdoor Furniture manufactures wood patio furniture. The company reported the following costs for December 2019.

Wood	$200,000
Nails and glue	11,000
Wood preserving stain	7,500
Depreciation on saws	3,000
Depreciation on delivery truck	2,200
Assembly line workers' wages	56,000
Salesman's auto lease	1,400
Indirect manufacturing labor	35,000

*Northwest treats the cost of nails, glue, wood preserving stains and the depreciation on saws as indirect manufacturing costs

Determine the Northwest's manufacturing overhead costs for December.

AP-2B LO 2 3 4

Buddy Company has just completed its first year of operations. During the year, Buddy Company purchased $500,000 of materials. The year-end balance reported in the raw materials account was $50,000. An amount of $30,000 worth of the raw materials consumed was considered as indirect materials and entered into manufacturing overhead.

Buddy Company incurred $450,000 in total direct labor wages during the year. Factory workers are paid $25 per hour. Total manufacturing overhead during the year amounted to $350,000, which was $30,000 less than estimated. Total factory worker hours were 10% less than estimated. Buddy Company's manufacturing overhead was allocated using direct labor hours as the allocation base. Buddy Company charges any over or underallocated manufacturing overhead to cost of goods sold.

During the year, Buddy Company started and completed Job 003. This job consumed 25% of the total direct direct materials used this year and 35% of the direct labor hours. Determine the total cost for Job 003.

_____
_____
_____
_____
_____
_____

AP-3B LO 3 4

A company estimated its manufacturing overhead to be $510,000 for the year, based on a normal capacity of 100,000 direct labor hours. At the end of the year, actual direct labor hours totalled to 105,000 while actual manufacturing overhead costs amounted to $540,000.

Required

a) Calculate the predetermined overhead rate.

_____
_____
_____

b) Determine the amount of over or underallocated overhead.

_____
_____
_____
_____

AP-4B LO 3 4

Deltor Limited accepted a special order. The total estimated manufacturing overhead for the company amounted to $5,900,000 and total estimated direct labor hours were 400,000. The company allocates the manufacturing overhead based on the number of direct labor hours. At the end of the period, the special order incurred $850,000 of direct materials and $910,000 of direct labor costs. On average, factory workers are being paid $25 per hour.

During the period, the company used $291,500 of indirect materials and $121,000 of indirect labor.

Required

a) Calculate allocated manufacturing overhead costs and provide the related journal entry.

Date	Account Title and Explanation	Debit	Credit

_____
_____

b) Provide the journal entries to record indirect materials and indirect labor costs. Assume payments have not been made yet.

Date	Account Title and Explanation	Debit	Credit

c) Use the cost of goods sold method to account for any under or overallocated manufacturing overhead costs.

Date	Account Title and Explanation	Debit	Credit

AP-5B LO 3 4

A manufacturing firm uses a predetermined manufacturing overhead rate to allocate overhead to individual jobs, based on machine hours required. At the beginning of 2019, the firm expected to incur the following:

Manufacturing Overhead Costs	$ 600,000
Direct Labor Cost	1,500,000
Machine Hours	75,000 hours

At the end of 2019, the firm had actually incurred:

Direct Labor Cost	$1,210,000
Depreciation on Manufacturing Property, Plant and Equipment	480,000
Sales Salaries	25,000
Delivery Drivers' Wages	15,000
Plant Janitors' Wages	10,000
Machine Hours	55,000 hours

Required

a) Calculate the firm's predetermined manufacturing overhead rate.

b) Post the manufacturing overhead transactions to the Manufacturing Overhead T-account and determine the amount of underallocated or overallocated overhead.

MANUFACTURING OVERHEAD

c) Close the manufacturing overhead account to cost of goods sold.

Date	Account Title and Explanation	Debit	Credit

AP-6B LO 2 3

QRS Manufacturing Company makes large drills for specific customers and uses job order costing to accumulate costs. The company started operating in January 2019 with no inventories. During January, it worked on two jobs.

	Job # 1	Job #2
Direct Material Used	$69,000	$45,000
Direct Labor @ $10 per hour	$35,000	$60,000

QRS incurred manufacturing overhead costs of $209,000. Budgeted monthly manufacturing overhead is $200,000.

The company uses a predetermined overhead rate based on 10,000 direct labor hours per month.

Required

a) Calculate the predetermined overhead rate per direct labor hour.

b) Determine the amounts of overhead to apply to each job.

AP-7B LO 2

StarPower Inc. is a company that produces custom photo frames. On April 15, 2019, StarPower Inc. records the transfer of $100,000 of raw materials into production. $24,000 of the raw materials is considered as direct materials, and $76,000 of the raw materials is considered as indirect materials. What is the journal entry to transfer these costs to the WIP and manufacturing overhead accounts?

Date	Account Title and Explanation	Debit	Credit

AP-8B LO 2

Johnson's Fancy Bakery worked on two projects during the month of April. Information on the jobs is given below:

23.5 BCM

50 BCL

	Birthday Cake	Wedding Cake	
Flour $2/lb	5 lb	12 lb	M
Eggs $2/dozen	0.5 dozen	1 dozen	M 46WCM
Sugar $2/lb	2.5 lb	4 lb	M
Other decorative ingredients $5/lb	1.5 lb	2.4 lb	M
Mixing $2/hour	4	4	L 71WCL
Decorating $7/hour	6	9	L
Manufacturing Overhead *	$70	$100	

*Actual cost

Required

a) Calculate direct materials and direct labor for each job.

BC flour = 10 WC flour = 24
BC eggs = 1 WC eggs = 2
BC Sugar = 5 WC sugar 8
BC ODI = 7.5 WC ODI = 12
BC Mixing = 8 WC Mixing = 8
BC decorating = 42 WC decorating = 63
BC total = 73.5 WC total = 117
43.5 difference

143.5

b) What is the total product cost for each job?

23.5 + 50 + 70 = ~~██████~~ BC

46 + 71 + 100 = 217   WC

AP-9B LO 5

Overhead Doors manufactures garage doors. The company has just finished an order for garage doors for a new subdivision being built by Landmark Homes. They have just completed and delivered 50 garage doors related to order #58742. Below are the financial details of the order on a per unit basis.

Sales Price $1,300
Direct Labor $300
Direct Material $400
Manufacturing Overhead $150

Using this information, prepare a Job Order Cost and Margin Record for this job.

AP-10B LO 5

XYZ Company had the following results of operation for its consulting business for the year 2019.

Number of Hours Provided	6,000
Rate of Service per Hour	$135.00
Billable Travel Cost	$240,000
Direct Labor Used	$300,000
Supplies & Other Overhead	$90,000

Calculate the gross profit and gross margin for the year.

Case Study

CS-1 [LO 1 2 3 4]

MW Clothing is a machine-intensive manufacturing company that produces clothes for many different retailers. The company recently finished working on an order from a customer, which consisted of 50 blue colored jeans with specifications of a 32-inch waist and 32-inch length. The following cost data relate to the manufacturing activities of MW Clothing for this order.

Direct Materials	$5,000
Direct Labor	2,300
Indirect Materials	500
Indirect Labor	1,000
Salaries, Administrative staff	10,000
Insurance, factory	150
Depreciation, factory	750
Utilities, factory	1,400
Direct Labor Hours	200 hours
Machine Hours	1,500 hours

*Factory insurance, depreciation and utilities' costs are considered indirect manufacturing overhead costs

Required

a) Why would job order costing be suitable to calculate the cost of this order?

_____

_____

b) Calculate the total manufacturing overhead costs incurred by the company.

_____

_____

_____

_____

_____

_____

c) At the beginning of the year, the company estimated that it would incur a total of $50,000 in manufacturing overhead costs, 2,800 direct labor hours, and 20,000 machine hours. The company uses predetermined overhead rates to apply overhead costs to production. Calculate the predetermined overhead rate for the company using direct labor hours as an allocation base.

_____

_____

d) Calculate the predetermined overhead rate for the company using machine hours as an allocation base.

_____

_____

e) Calculate the total overhead cost that will be allocated to this job, using the predetermined overhead rates calculated in both part c) and d).

_____

_____

f) Which allocation base results in a smaller variance between actual and estimated manufacturing overhead? Which allocation base should the company use to calculate the predetermined overhead rate? Explain why.

_____

_____

_____

_____

_____

_____

_____

_____

_____

_____

_____

_____

g) How would we account for the underallocation of manufacturing under the cost of goods sold method?

_____

_____

_____

Critical Thinking

CT-1 LO 1 4

Governments often contract with suppliers for unique items (e.g. military equipment) on a cost plus basis. Cost plus pricing is one where the contractor is reimbursed for the cost of completing the contract plus a mark-up on computed cost.

In a cost plus contracting environment, what is the contractor's motivation when deciding the rate to be used to allocate manufacturing overhead to the job? In other words, would the contractor prefer a higher or lower rate?

Chapter 3

PROCESS COSTING

LEARNING OBJECTIVES

LO 1 Describe the physical flow of units in process costing and explain conversion costs

LO 2 Calculate equivalent units of production

LO 3 Perform inventory valuations using weighted-average cost

LO 4 Prepare journal entries for transferred units

LO 5 Describe ethics related to estimation of equivalent units

Appendix

LO 6 Perform inventory valuations using FIFO

AMEENGAGE™ *Access ameengage.com for integrated resources including tutorials, practice exercises, the digital textbook and more.*

Assessment Questions

AS-1 LO 1

When should process costing be used?

_____

_____

AS-2 LO 1

In job order costing, a work-in-process is maintained for each job. How is the work-in-process (WIP) account maintained in process costing?

_____

_____

AS-3 LO 1

Provide the formula for calculating the number of units in ending inventory.

_____

_____

AS-4 LO 1

In process costing, what type of costs does each work-in-process (WIP) account include?

_____

_____

_____

AS-5 LO 1

Define conversion costs.

_____

_____

AS-6 LO 1

Provide an example of a conversion cost.

_____

_____

_____

AS-7 LO 1

How are conversion costs different from direct material costs?

_____

_____

_____

_____

AS-8 LO 2

Why is it necessary to calculate equivalent units of production?

_____

_____

_____

AS-9 LO 3

Consider a process in which all direct materials are added right at the beginning of the process. What is the degree of completion with respect to direct materials for partially completed products in the department's ending inventory?

_____

_____

_____

AS-10 LO 3

Why do most companies prefer to use the weighted-average cost method?

_____

_____

_____

_____

_____

AS-11 [LO 4]

What is the journal entry to transfer costs from the first department to the second department when process costing is used?

_____

_____

AS-12 [LO 5]

What is the purpose of a cost of production report?

_____

_____

_____

_____

_____

AS-13 [LO 5]

Why is it important to estimate the percentage completion in ending work-in-process inventory with unbiased integrity?

_____

_____

AS-14 [LO 2 6]

When calculating equivalent units, which inventory valuation method requires a separation of beginning inventory units and units started and completed?

_____

_____

AS-15 [LO 1 6]

If conversion costs decrease over time, which inventory valuation method will result in a higher cost of goods sold?

_____

_____

AS-16 [LO 3 6]

What is the main difference between the first-in-first-out (FIFO) and weighted-average methods?

_____

_____

_____

_____

Application Questions Group A

AP-1A LO 4

Provide journal entries for each of the following process costing transactions:

June 5	$8,000 worth of direct materials were entered into the assembly department from storage.
June 30	$50,000 worth of completed goods were transferred from the assembly department into finished goods inventory.

Date	Account Title and Explanation	Debit	Credit

AP-2A LO 4

The production process at Wool Inc., a manufacturing firm, includes a cleaning department and a spinning department. Prepare the corresponding journal entries for each of the transactions below. Note that manufacturing wages are recorded in the wages payable account and that Wool records depreciation in the accumulated depreciation account.

July 1	Purchase of $90,000 worth of raw materials on account
July 3	Direct materials worth $50,000 were sent to the cleaning department
July 31	Cleaning department's labor wage liability incurred $40,000 for direct labor
July 31	Allocated $35,000 of manufacturing overhead to the cleaning department.
July 31	Cleaning department transferred 100,000 units at a cost of $60,000 to the spinning department

Assume the company has not made any payments.

Date	Account Title and Explanation	Debit	Credit

Date	Account Title and Explanation	Debit	Credit

AP-3A LO 1

Key Co. had 3,000 units in work-in-process on January 1, 2019. During the month of January, 10,000 units were completed and transferred out. At the end of the month, 4,000 units remained in work-in-process. How many units were started during January?

Unit Calculations	◄—— Inputs ——►			=	◄—— Outputs ——►		Total Outputs
	Beginning WIP Inventory	Add Current Month	Equals Total Production		Subtract Completed Transfer Out	+ Ending WIP Inventory	
Whole Units							

AP-4A LO 2

Giada Company has 2,000 units of beginning inventory in their WIP which are 70% complete with respect to conversion costs. During the period, 23,000 units were completed and transferred leaving 3,000 units in the WIP at the end of the period. Ending inventory is only one-third complete with respect to conversion costs. Both beginning and ending inventory are 100% complete with respect to direct materials. Assume that the weighted-average method is used.

Calculate the equivalent units of production for direct materials and conversion costs.

Unit Calculations	◄—— Inputs ——►			=	◄—— Outputs ——►		Total Outputs
	Beginning WIP Inventory	Add Current Month	Equals Total Production		Subtract Completed Transfer Out	+ Ending WIP Inventory	
Direct Materials Units							
% Equivalent Completed							
Conversion Equivalent Units							

AP-5A [LO 6]

For the current period, Alcuin Company computed 50,000 equivalent units of production for materials. WIP beginning is 75% complete as to conversion cost and 100% complete as to materials, while WIP ending is 75% complete per conversion cost and 100% complete per materials. During the period, Alcuin completed and transferred out a total of 49,000 units of output. The company started and completed 45,000 units in the current period. Assume Alcuin uses FIFO method for inventory valuation.

Required

a) How many units remained in its ending inventory?

_____

_____

_____

	← Inputs →				← Outputs →			
	Beginning WIP Inventory	Add Current Month	Equals Total Production	=	Subtract Completed Transfer Out		+ Ending WIP Inventory	Total Outputs
Unit Calculations					From Beg. Inv.	From Current Month		
Direct Materials Whole Units								
% Equivalent								
Direct Materials Equivalent Units								

b) Determine equivalent units with respect to conversion costs for beginning inventory.

_____

_____

_____

	← Inputs →			=	← Outputs →			
	Beginning WIP Inventory	Add Current Month	Equals Total Production		Subtract Completed Transfer Out		+ Ending WIP Inventory	Total Outputs
Unit Calculations					From Beg. Inv.	From Current Month		
Conversion Whole Units								
% Equivalent								
Conversion Cost Equivalent Units								

c)   Determine the total equivalent units with respect to conversion cost.

Unit Calculations	Inputs			=	Outputs		
	Beginning WIP Inventory	+ Add Current Month	Equals Total Production		Subtract Completed Transfer Out	+ Ending WIP Inventory	Total Outputs
					From Beg. Inv. From Current Month		
Conversion Whole Units							
% Equivalent							
Conversion Cost Equivalent Units							

AP-6A LO 2

Calvez Manufacturing Inc. uses the weighted average cost method under the process costing system. Some numbers are missing from the following forming department's equivalent unit calculation table.

Unit Calculations	Inputs			=	Outputs		
	Beginning WIP Inventory	+ Add Current Month	Equals Total Production		Subtract Completed Transfer Out	+ Ending WIP Inventory	Total Outputs
Whole Units	(a)	180,000	(b)	=	(c)	40,000	200,000
% Equivalent Completed					(d)	(f)	
Equivalent Units					(e)	10,000	(g)

Required

Calculate the following missing numbers:
a)   Number of whole units of beginning WIP inventory: _____
b)   Number of total whole units that went through the production process: _____
c)   Number of whole units that are completed and transferred out: _____
d)   Percentage of completion for units that are completed and transferred out: _____
e)   Number of equivalent units that are completed and transferred out: _____
f)   Percentage of completion for ending WIP inventory: _____
g)   Number of equivalent units for the current period: _____

AP-7A LO 2 6

Meow Meow Mfg. Corporation produces standardized cat litter boxes. As of October 31, 2019, Meow Meow's assembly department has provided the following information:

Beginning inventory*	40,000 units
Started during the month	300,000 units
Ending inventory**	60,000 units

*Degree of Completion: 70% completed by September 30, 2019
** Degree of Completion: 80% completed by October 31, 2019

Required

a) Calculate the number of equivalent units for October 2019 using the FIFO method.

Unit Calculations	Inputs			=	Outputs				
	Beginning WIP Inventory	Add Current Month	Equals Total Production		Subtract Completed Transfer Out From Beg. Inv.	From Current Month	+ Ending WIP Inventory	Total Outputs	
Whole Units									
% Equivalent									
Equivalent Units									

b) Repeat part a) using the weighted-average method.

Unit Calculations	Inputs			=	Outputs		
	Beginning WIP Inventory	Add Current Month	Equals Total Production		Subtract Completed Transfer Out	+ Ending WIP Inventory	Total Outputs
Whole Units							
% Equivalent Completed							
Equivalent Units							

AP-8A LO 1 2 3

Francis Steel Company is a steel manufacturer. It has two departments. Department A is responsible for melting the scrap metal. Afterwards, the molten metals are transferred to Department B. Department B will then pour the molten metal into ingot casting. Ingot castings are transferred to finished goods inventory for shipment to customers. Data for Department A for January 2019 are:

Costs of Beginning Work-in-Process - January 1	
Department A	
Scrap Metal	$6,000
Labor work required to melt the metal and operate the furnace	$5,000
Factory Overhead (including utilities rent and costs to run the furnace)	$500

Costs Added in January	
Department A	
Scrap Metal	$80,000
Labor	$130,000
Factory Overhead	$4,500

Jan.1, 60% complete as to conversion costs	5,000 tons
The amount of scrap metal added to Department A in January	67,000 tons
The amount of molten metals transferred to Department B	68,000 tons
Jan. 31, 50% complete as to conversion costs	4,000 tons

For material and conversion costs, calculate the cost per equivalent unit for department B under the weighted average method.

Francis Steel Company
Cost of Production Report
Department A: January 2019

Unit Calculations	Inputs Beginning WIP Inventory	Add Current Month	Equals Total Production	=	Outputs Completed Transfer Out	Add Ending WIP Inventory	Total Outputs
Direct Materials Whole Units							
% Equivalent Completed							
Conversion Equivalent Units							

Cost Calculations	Inputs Beginning WIP Inventory	Add Current Month	Equals Total Cost of Production	Cost of Production Per Unit	Outputs Subtract Completed Transfer Out	= Ending WIP Inventory	Check Total Outputs =Total Inputs
Direct Materials Units							
Direct Materials Costs							
Conversion Units							
Direct Labor							
Manufacturing Overhead							
Total Conversion Cost							
Total							

_____

_____

_____

_____

_____

_____

_____

_____

_____

_____

_____

_____

AP-9A LO 2 3 6

Barney Corporation adds materials at the beginning of the process in Department AX. The conversion costs were 75% complete as to the 20,000 units in WIP on April 30 and 50% complete as to the 15,000 units in WIP on May 31. During May, 55,000 units were completed and transferred to the next department. An analysis of the costs relating to WIP at May 1 and to production activity for May is as follows:

	Costs	
	Direct Materials	**Conversion**
WIP, May 1	$ 16,600	$ 14,800
Costs added in May	75,700	33,300

Required

a) Prepare Department AX's cost of production report for May assuming FIFO was used. Under FIFO, what is the cost per equivalent unit with respect to direct materials? What is the cost per equivalent unit with respect to conversion costs?

Barney Corporation
Cost of Production Report (FIFO)
Department AX: May 2019

	◄─── Inputs ───►			=	◄─────── Outputs ───────►		
	Beginning Cutting Inventory	+ Add Current Month	Equals Total Production		Subtract Completed Transfer Out		+ Ending WIP Inventory	Total Outputs
Unit Calculations					From Beg. Inv.	From Current Month		
Direct Materials Whole Units								
% Equivalent								
Direct Materials Equivalent Unit								
Conversion Equivalent Units								
% Equivalent								
Conversion Cost Equivalent Unit								

	◄─── Inputs ───►				◄─────── Outputs ───────►			Check Total Outputs =Total Inputs
	Beginning WIP Inventory	+ Add Current Month	Equals Total Production	Cost per Unit (Current Period)	Subtract Completed Transfer Out		= Ending WIP Inventory	
Cost Calculations					From Beg. Inv.	From Current Month	Total Transferred Out	
Direct Materials Equivalent Units								
Direct Materials Cost Incurred this Period								
Direct Materials Cost from Last period								
Total Direct Materials Cost Transferred Out								
Conversion Equivalent Units								
Total Conversion Cost Incurred this Period								
Conversion Cost from Last Period								
Total Conversion Cost Transferred Out								
Total Cost Accounted for								

_____
_____
_____
_____

b) Repeat part a) but using the weighted average inventory system instead.

	Barney Corporation Cost of Production Report (WAC) Department AX: May 2019							
	← Inputs →			=	← Outputs →			
Unit Calculations	Beginning WIP Inventory	Add Current Month	Equals Total Production		Completed Transfer Out	Add Ending WIP Inventory	Total Outputs	
Direct Materials Whole Units								
% Equivalent Completed								
Conversion Equivalent Units								
	← Inputs →				← Outputs →			
Cost Calculations	Beginning WIP Inventory	Add Current Month	Equals Total Cost of Production	Cost of Production Per Unit	Subtract Completed Transfer Out	= Ending WIP Inventory	Check Total Outputs =Total Inputs	
Direct Materials Units								
Direct Materials Costs								
Conversion Units								
Total Conversion Cost								
Total								

_____
_____
_____
_____
_____

AP-10A LO 2 3

Catridge Company uses the weighted average cost method under process costing. It has no beginning work in process inventory. By the end of the period, the company has transferred 9,000 units to finished goods and kept 3,000 units in the work in process inventory. Ending WIP inventory is fully completed as to direct material cost and 1/3 completed in terms of conversion costs. The company has incurred $48,000 of direct materials and $66,000 of conversion costs.

Required

a) Determine the equivalent units for materials and conversion costs.

Unit Calculations	Inputs			=	Outputs		
	Beginning WIP Inventory	Add Current Month	Equals Total Production		Completed Transfer Out	Add Ending WIP Inventory	Total Outputs
Direct Materials Whole Units							
% Equivalent Completed							
Conversion Equivalent Units							

b) Determine the cost per equivalent unit for direct materials and conversion costs, total cost transferred to finished goods, and total cost of ending WIP inventory.

Cost Calculations	Inputs			Cost of Production Per Unit	Outputs		Check
	Beginning WIP Inventory	Add Current Month	Equals Total Cost of Production		Subtract Completed Transfer Out	= Ending WIP Inventory	Total Outputs =Total Inputs
Direct Materials Units							
Direct Materials Costs							
Conversion Units							
Total Conversion Cost							
Total							

Application Questions Group B

AP-1B LO 4

Shown below is a list of costs incurred by Candle Lite Inc. for the month of May. The production process in Candle Lite involves three departments (mixing, moulding and packaging). Prepare the journal entries to record the costs of direct materials, direct labor and manufacturing overhead for the packaging department. Also prepare the journal entries related to costs transferred into and out of the packaging department.

Direct Materials put into production	$30,000
Mixing – 55%	
Moulding –15%	
Packaging – 30%	
Direct Labor Cost incurred but not paid	$15,000
Mixing – 40%	
Moulding –35%	
Packaging – 25%	
Allocation of Manufacturing Overhead	
Mixing	$5000
Moulding	8,800
Packaging	9,000
Cost Transferred from one department to the next	
Mixing to Moulding	$6,000
Moulding to Packaging	10,000
Packaging to Finished Goods Inventory	5,000

Prepare journal entries for the packaging department.

Date	Account Title and Explanation	Debit	Credit

Date	Account Title and Explanation	Debit	Credit

AP-2B LO 4

Clean Water had the following process costing transactions in March:

Mar 5	Purchased and paid $6,500 for raw materials.
Mar 15	Made a payment of $50,000 for total manufacturing payroll which was accrued for in February in the wages payable account.
Mar 31	Filtration department incurred $10,000 of direct labor wages.
Mar 31	Bottling department incurred $4,000 of direct labor wages.
Mar 31	Transfer costs of $9,000 from filtration department to bottling department.
Mar 31	Transfer costs of $12,000 from bottling department to finished goods inventory.

Record the above transactions in the general journal.

Date	Account Title and Explanation	Debit	Credit

AP-3B LO 1 2

Katrisse Company employs process costing and uses the weighted-average method to cost its inventory. Raw materials are added at the beginning of the process. At the beginning of the period, the company had 450 units in its work in process inventory. Of that amount, 60% was complete with respect to conversion costs. In addition, the company started another 1,300 units during the period. Ignore transferred-in costs.

Required

a)   If Katrisse finished and transferred out 1,175 units to finished goods, how many units were in ending inventory?

Unit Calculations	← Inputs →			=	← Outputs →		
	Beginning WIP Inventory	Add Current Month	Equals Total Production		Subtract Completed Transfer Out	+ Ending WIP Inventory	Total Outputs
Direct Materials Units							

b)   What are the equivalent units of production for materials and conversion costs, assuming that the ending inventory is 50% complete as to conversion cost?

Unit Calculations	← Inputs →			=	← Outputs →		
	Beginning WIP Inventory	Add Current Month	Equals Total Production		Subtract Completed Transfer Out	+ Ending WIP Inventory	Total Outputs
Direct Materials Units							
% Equivalent Completed							
Conversion Equivalent Units							

AP-4B LO 2 3

Kayles Company uses a weighted-average process costing system and started 30,000 units this month. Kayles had 12,000 units that were 30% complete as to conversion costs in beginning work in process inventory and 3,000 units that were 60% complete as to conversion costs in ending work in process inventory.

Required

a)   What are equivalent units of production with respect to conversion costs?

Unit Calculations	Inputs			=	Outputs		
	Beginning WIP Inventory	Add Current Month	Equals Total Production		Subtract Completed Transfer Out	+ Ending WIP Inventory	Total Outputs
Direct Materials Units							
% Equivalent Completed							
Conversion Equivalent Units							

---

b) If the Kayles Company assigned $43,200 of conversion cost to its previous month's ending inventory and incurred an additional conversion cost of $101,100 during this month, compute the cost per equivalent unit with respect to conversion costs.

Per Unit Cost Calculations	Inputs			Cost of Production Per Unit
	Beginning WIP Inventory	Add Current Month	Equals Total Cost of Production	
Conversion Units				
Conversion Cost				

AP-5B LO 6

Bonne Company uses a process costing system. The casting department manager provides the following information for October:

	WIP October 1		WIP October 31	Costs
	Degree of Completion	Costs	Degree of Completion	Added in October
Direct Materials	80%	$4,000	90%	$66,000
Conversion Costs	90%	$10,000	20%	$312,000

The casting department had a beginning WIP inventory and ending WIP inventory of 400 and 800 units, respectively. It started 11,000 units into production during the month. The company uses the FIFO method.

Required

a) What is the number of equivalent units with respect to direct materials and conversion costs?

	Inputs			=	Outputs		
	Beginning WIP Inventory	Add Current Month	Equals Total Production		Subtract Completed Transfer Out	+ Ending WIP Inventory	Total Outputs
Unit Calculations					From Beg. Inv. From Current Month		
Direct Materials Whole Units							
% Equivalent							
Direct Materials Equivalent Units							
Conversion Whole Units							
% Equivalent							
Conversion Cost Equivalent Units							

_____

_____

b) What are the material cost per equivalent unit and conversion cost per equivalent unit? How much are the total costs transferred out and total costs of the ending WIP inventory?

	Inputs				Outputs				Check Total
	Beginning WIP Inventory	Add Current Month	Equals Total Production	Cost per Unit (Current Period)	Subtract Completed Transfer Out			= Ending WIP Inventory	Outputs =Total Inputs
Cost Calculations					From Beg. Inv.	From Current Month	Total Transferred Out		
Direct Materials Equivalent Units	80	10,920	11,000	1	200	10,080		720	11,000
Direct Materials Cost Incurred this Period		$66,000	$66,000	$6.00	$1,200	$60,480		$4,320	$66,000
Direct Materials Cost from Last period	$4,000		$4,000		$4,000				$4,000
Total Direct Materials Cost Transferred Out							$65,680		
Conversion Equivalent Units	40	10,360	10,400	1	40	10,200		160	10,400
Conversion Cost Incurred this Period		$312,000	$312,000	$30.00	$1,200	$306,000		$4,800	$312,000
Conversion Cost from Last Period	$10,000		$10,000		$10,000				$10,000
Total Conversion Cost Transferred Out							$317,200		
Total Cost Accounted for	$14,000	$378,000	$392,000		$16,400	$366,480	$382,880	$9,120	$392,000

_____

_____

_____

_____

AP-6B LO 2 6

Department A is the first stage of JL Company's production cycle. The following information is available for conversion costs for the month of April 2008:

	Units
Work-in-Process, beginning (60% complete)	20,000
Started in April	340,000
Completed in April and transferred to Department B	320,000
Work-in-Process, ending (40% complete)	40,000

Required

a) Using the FIFO method, determine the equivalent units of production with respect to conversion costs.

	← Inputs →			=	← Outputs →		
	Beginning WIP Inventory	Add Current Month	Equals Total Production		Subtract Completed Transfer Out	+ Ending WIP Inventory	Total Outputs
Unit Calculations					From Beg. Inv.	From Current Month	
Conversion Costs Whole Units							
% Equivalent							
Conversion Costs Equivalent Units							

b) Using the weighted average method, determine equivalent units of production with respect to conversion costs.

	← Inputs →			=	← Outputs →		
Unit Calculations	Beginning WIP Inventory	Add Current Month	Equals Total Production		Subtract Completed Transfer Out	+ Ending WIP Inventory	Total Outputs
Whole Units							
% Equivalent Completed							
Equivalent Units							

AP-7B LO 2 6

Department Y of Sweepstakes Manufacturing Corporation showed the following data regarding their production for the month just ended:

WIP, beginning, 61.50% complete for conversion costs	14,000 units
Started this month	32,000 units
Transferred to Department Z	29,000 units
WIP, ending – 50% complete for conversion costs	17,000 units

Required

a)   Calculate Department Y's equivalent unit production for the month using FIFO method.

Unit Calculations	Inputs			=	Outputs		
	Beginning WIP Inventory	Add Current Month	Equals Total Production		Subtract Completed Transfer Out	+ Ending WIP Inventory	Total Outputs
					From Beg. Inv.	From Current Month	
Whole Units							
% Equivalent							
Equivalent Units							

b)   Repeat part a) using the weighted average method instead.

Unit Calculations	Inputs			=	Outputs		
	Beginning WIP Inventory	Add Current Month	Equals Total Production		Subtract Completed Transfer Out	+ Ending WIP Inventory	Total Outputs
Whole Units							
% Equivalent Completed							
Equivalent Units							

AP-8B LO 1 2 3 6

Q-toric Company manufactures a single product, mushroom soup, which undergoes three production processes (in order: chopping, mixing and packaging) before it can be transferred to finished goods. In the month of February, the chopping department incurred $10,500 and $8,000 for material cost and conversion cost respectively during the month. Beginning inventory was 50% complete as to conversion costs and materials are added at the beginning of the period at each department. Beginning work in process inventory has 7,000 units, which are attached with $3,500 material costs and $2,500 conversion costs. The chopping department started 14,000 units during the period. There are 3,000 units remaining in the chopping process at the end of the month, which are 60% complete as to conversion cost.

Required

a)   Calculate the number of units transferred from the chopping department to the mixing department.

Unit Calculations	Inputs			=	Outputs		
	Beginning WIP Inventory	Add Current Month	Equals Total Production		Subtract Completed Transfer Out	+ Ending WIP Inventory	Total Outputs
Whole Units							

b) Using the weighted average costing method, calculate the equivalent units for material and conversion costs.

Unit Calculations	Beginning WIP Inventory	+ Add Current Month	Equals Total Production	=	Subtract Completed Transfer Out	+ Ending WIP Inventory	Total Outputs
Direct Materials Units							
% Equivalent Completed							
Conversion Equivalent Units							

c) For material and conversion costs, calculate the cost per equivalent unit.

Cost Calculations	Beginning WIP Inventory	Add Current Month	Equals Total Cost of Production	Cost of Production Per Unit	Subtract Completed Transfer Out	= Ending WIP Inventory	Check Total Outputs =Total Inputs
Direct Materials Units							
Direct Materials Cost							
Conversion Units							
Conversion Cost							
Total Cost							

d) Now assume that the beginning inventory is 50% complete as to materials and 0% complete as to conversion costs. Materials are 75% complete and conversion costs are 60% complete for ending inventory. Calculate the equivalent units for direct materials and conversion costs using FIFO method.

Unit Calculations	Beginning Cutting Inventory	Add Current Month	Equals Total Production	=	Subtract Completed Transfer Out — From Beg. Inv.	From Current Month	+ Ending WIP Inventory	Total Outputs
Direct Materials Whole Units								
% Equivalent								
Direct Materials Equivalent Unit								
Conversion Equivalent Units								
% Equivalent								
Conversion Cost Equivalent Unit								

AP-9B LO 2 3 6

Sajulga Canning Corporation prepares canned tuna and incurred the following costs for the month of March 2019:

Direct Materials			$256,000
Direct Labor:	Loining Department	35,000 hours @ $13 per hour	
	Cooking Department	25,000 hours @ $15 per hour	
	Canning Department	10,000 hours @ $16 per hour	
	Labelling Department	20,000 hours @ $5 per hour	
Manufacturing Overhead:	Loining Department		$15,000
	Cooking Department		$12,000
	Canning Department		$15,000
	Labelling Department		$16,000

Required

a) For each department, calculate the conversion cost.

Department	Loining	Cooking	Canning	Labelling

Consider parts b) and c) below independently

b) All materials are added in the loining department. With regards to the loining department, 250,000 cans of tuna were completed and 50,000 cans were remaining in the department's production area at the end of March. These remaining cans of tuna are 60% complete as to conversion costs. The department has no beginning inventory. Calculate the loining department's cost per equivalent unit with respect to direct materials and conversion costs using the weighted-average cost method.

Sajulga Canning Corporation **Cost of Production Report (WAC)** **Loining Department: March 2019**							
	←——— Inputs ———→			=	←——— Outputs ———→		
Unit Calculations	Beginning WIP Inventory	Add Current Month	Equals Total Production		Completed Transfer Out	Add Ending WIP Inventory	Total Outputs
Direct Materials Units							
% Equivalent Completed							
Conversion Equivalent Units							
	←——— Inputs ———→				←——— Outputs ———→		
Cost Calculations	Beginning WIP Inventory	Add Current Month	Equals Total Cost of Production	Cost of Production Per Unit	Subtract Completed Transfer Out	= Ending WIP Inventory	*Check* Total Outputs =Total Inputs
Direct Materials Units							
Direct Materials Costs							
Conversion Units							
Direct Labor							
Manufacturing Overhead							
Total Conversion Cost							
Total							

_____

_____

_____

_____

_____

_____

_____

_____

_____

_____

_____

_____

_____

_____

_____

_____

_____

_____

c) All materials are added immediately at the very beginning of the loining process. At the beginning of the period, there are 100,000 units (40% complete with respect to conversion costs) which cost $120,000. Of this amount, $70,000 is for materials and $50,000 is for conversion costs. During the month of March, the department started and completed 250,000 cans of tuna chunks and was left with 50,000 cans in its ending inventory. 60% of the ending inventory is complete in terms of conversion costs. For each inventory valuation method (i.e. weighted average and FIFO), determine the cost per equivalent unit with respect to direct materials and conversion costs.

<u>Weighted average method</u>

<table>
<tr><td colspan="9" align="center">Sajulga Canning Corporation
Cost of Production Report (WAC)
Loining Department: March 2019</td></tr>
<tr><td rowspan="2">Unit Calculations</td><td colspan="3" align="center">◄──── Inputs ────►</td><td>=</td><td colspan="3" align="center">◄──── Outputs ────►</td><td></td></tr>
<tr><td>Beginning WIP Inventory</td><td>Add Current Month</td><td>Equals Total Production</td><td></td><td>Completed Transfer Out</td><td>Add Ending WIP Inventory</td><td>Total Outputs</td></tr>
<tr><td>Direct Materials Units</td><td></td><td></td><td></td><td></td><td></td><td></td><td></td></tr>
<tr><td>% Equivalent Completed</td><td></td><td></td><td></td><td></td><td></td><td></td><td></td></tr>
<tr><td>Conversion Equivalent Units</td><td></td><td></td><td></td><td></td><td></td><td></td><td></td></tr>
<tr><td rowspan="2">Cost Calculations</td><td colspan="3" align="center">◄──── Inputs ────►</td><td></td><td colspan="3" align="center">◄──── Outputs ────►</td></tr>
<tr><td>Beginning WIP Inventory</td><td>Add Current Month</td><td>Equals Total Cost of Production</td><td>Cost of Production Per Unit</td><td>Subtract Completed Transfer Out</td><td>= Ending WIP Inventory</td><td>Check Total Outputs =Total Inputs</td></tr>
<tr><td>Direct Materials Units</td><td></td><td></td><td></td><td></td><td></td><td></td><td></td></tr>
<tr><td>Direct Materials Costs</td><td></td><td></td><td></td><td></td><td></td><td></td><td></td></tr>
<tr><td></td><td></td><td></td><td></td><td></td><td></td><td></td><td></td></tr>
<tr><td>Conversion Units</td><td></td><td></td><td></td><td></td><td></td><td></td><td></td></tr>
<tr><td>Total Conversion Cost</td><td></td><td></td><td></td><td></td><td></td><td></td><td></td></tr>
<tr><td>Total</td><td></td><td></td><td></td><td></td><td></td><td></td><td></td></tr>
</table>

FIFO method

	Inputs			=	Outputs			
Unit Calculations	Beginning Cutting Inventory	Add Current Month	Equals Total Production		Subtract Completed Transfer Out — From Beg. Inv.	From Current Month	+ Ending WIP Inventory	Total Outputs
Direct Materials Whole Units								
% Equivalent								
Direct Materials Equivalent Unit								
Conversion Equivalent Units								
% Equivalent								
Conversion Cost Equivalent Unit								

	Inputs			Cost per Unit (Current Period)	Outputs			= Ending WIP Inventory	Check Total Outputs =Total Inputs
Cost Calculations	Beginning WIP Inventory	Add Current Month	Equals Total Production		Subtract Completed Transfer Out — From Beg. Inv.	From Current Month	Total Transferred Out		
Direct Materials Equivalent Units									
Direct Materials Cost Incurred this Period									
Direct Materials Cost from Last period									
Total Direct Materials Cost Transferred Out									
Conversion Equivalent Units									
Total Conversion Cost Incurred this Period									
Conversion Cost from Last Period									
Total Conversion Cost Transferred Out									
Total Cost Accounted for									

AP-10B LO 2 3

Catty Manufacturing added 26,000 units, and completed and transferred out 30,000 units of mini-electric fan from its painting department in the current period. Relevant information for the painting department is presented below:

	Units	Degree of Completion*
WIP Inventory – Beginning	10,000	90%
WIP Inventory – Ending	?	80%

*This degree of completion corresponds to conversion costs only. Note that ending WIP inventory is 100% complete with respect to direct materials costs.

Additional information:

- WIP Inventory beginning has $3,500 worth of material cost and $4,000 conversion cost.
- During the period, Catty incurred additional $10,900 of material costs and $12,100 of conversion costs.

Required

Calculate the cost per equivalent unit with respect to direct materials and conversion costs, total cost transferred to finished goods, and total cost of ending WIP inventory.

Unit Calculations	Beginning WIP Inventory	Add Current Month	Equals Total Production	=	Completed Transfer Out	Add Ending WIP Inventory	Total Outputs
	◄——— Inputs ———►				◄——— Outputs ———►		
Direct Materials Whole Units							
% Equivalent Completed							
Conversion Equivalent Units							
	◄——— Inputs ———►				◄——— Outputs ———►		
Cost Calculations	Beginning WIP Inventory	Add Current Month	Equals Total Cost of Production	Cost of Production Per Unit	Subtract Completed Transfer Out	= Ending WIP Inventory	Check Total Outputs =Total Inputs
Direct Materials Units							
Direct Materials Costs							
Conversion Units							
Total Conversion Cost							
Total							

_____

_____

_____

_____

_____

_____

_____

Case Study

CS-1 LO 1 2 3 4

The finishing department of Diana Company produced 40,000 units of standard chairs during the month of February. It incurred $15,000 in direct materials cost; 2,500 direct labor hours paid at $10 per hour; and manufacturing overhead applied at 150% of direct labor cost. Diana Company uses process costing to accumulate costs. Assume there is no beginning inventory.

Required

a) Calculate the conversion costs incurred during the month of February.

b) Assume, that only 30,000 units were completed and transferred out. The remaining 10,000 units left in ending inventory are only 70% complete with respect to conversion costs. Direct materials are added at the beginning of the process. Prepare a cost of production report.

<table>
<tr><td colspan="9" align="center">Diana Company
Cost of Production Report</td></tr>
<tr><td rowspan="2"></td><td colspan="3" align="center">◄──── Inputs ────►</td><td align="center">=</td><td colspan="3" align="center">◄──── Outputs ────►</td></tr>
<tr><td align="center">Beginning
Cutting
Inventory</td><td align="center">Add
Current
Month</td><td align="center">Equals
Total
Production</td><td></td><td align="center">Completed
Transfer Out</td><td align="center">Add Ending
WIP
Inventory</td><td align="center">Total Outputs</td></tr>
<tr><td>Unit Calculations</td><td></td><td></td><td></td><td></td><td></td><td></td><td></td></tr>
<tr><td>Direct Materials Whole Units</td><td></td><td></td><td></td><td></td><td></td><td></td><td></td></tr>
<tr><td>% Equivalent Completed</td><td></td><td></td><td></td><td></td><td></td><td></td><td></td></tr>
<tr><td>Conversion Equivalent Units</td><td></td><td></td><td></td><td></td><td></td><td></td><td></td></tr>
<tr><td rowspan="2"></td><td colspan="3" align="center">◄──── Inputs ────►</td><td></td><td colspan="3" align="center">◄──── Outputs ────►</td></tr>
<tr><td align="center">Beginning
Cutting
Inventory</td><td align="center">Add
Current
Month</td><td align="center">Equals
Total Cost
of Production</td><td align="center">Cost of
Production
Per Unit</td><td align="center">Subtract
Completed
Transfer Out</td><td align="center">= Ending
WIP
Inventory</td><td align="center">Check
Total Outputs
=Total Inputs</td></tr>
<tr><td>Cost Calculations</td><td></td><td></td><td></td><td></td><td></td><td></td><td></td></tr>
<tr><td>Direct Materials Units</td><td></td><td></td><td></td><td></td><td></td><td></td><td></td></tr>
<tr><td>Direct Materials Costs</td><td></td><td></td><td></td><td></td><td></td><td></td><td></td></tr>
<tr><td></td><td></td><td></td><td></td><td></td><td></td><td></td><td></td></tr>
<tr><td>Conversion Units</td><td></td><td></td><td></td><td></td><td></td><td></td><td></td></tr>
<tr><td>Direct Labor</td><td></td><td></td><td></td><td></td><td></td><td></td><td></td></tr>
<tr><td>Manufacturing Overhead</td><td></td><td></td><td></td><td></td><td></td><td></td><td></td></tr>
<tr><td>Total Conversion Cost</td><td></td><td></td><td></td><td></td><td></td><td></td><td></td></tr>
<tr><td>Total</td><td></td><td></td><td></td><td></td><td></td><td></td><td></td></tr>
</table>

c) Refer to the cost of production report in part b. What are the cost per equivalent unit with respect to direct materials and conversion costs, the total costs transferred out to finished goods inventory, and the value of inventory at the end of February?

_____

_____

_____

_____

_____

d) Refer to the cost of production report in part b. Provide the journal entry to record direct materials, direct labor and manufacturing overhead. Also provide the journal entry to record the transfer of goods out of WIP and into finished goods inventory.

Date	Account Title and Explanation	Debit	Credit

Notes

Chapter 4

COST MANAGEMENT STRATEGIES

LEARNING OBJECTIVES

LO 1 Explain the importance of cost management strategies

LO 2 Explain the purpose of activity-based costing (ABC)

LO 3 Apply activity-based costing

LO 4 Describe just in time (JIT) manufacturing and the JIT inventory system

LO 5 Identify the seven areas of waste according to lean manufacturing

LO 6 Describe the four costs of producing quality products

LO 7 Explain the importance of the competence aspect of ethics in applying ABC and managing quality

AMEENGAGE *Access **ameengage.com** for integrated resources including tutorials, practice exercises, the digital textbook and more.*

——— Assessment Questions ———

AS-1 LO 1

How will inventory affect a company's cash flow?

AS-2 LO 1

Define inventory shrinkage.

AS-3 LO 1

How will inventory shrinkage affect the income statement and the balance sheet?

AS-4 LO 1

Identify a potential problem when a business holds high levels of inventory.

AS-5 `LO 2`

Define activity-based costing.

_____

_____

_____

AS-6 `LO 2`

In the past, overhead costs were allocated based on either direct labor hours or machine hours. Explain why these methods are becoming less popular.

_____

_____

_____

_____

_____

AS-7 `LO 1`

What is a cost allocation base?

_____

_____

_____

AS-8 `LO 3`

Provide the formula for the predetermined overhead rate.

_____

_____

AS-9 `LO 3`

What is the difference between using a single predetermined overhead rate to cost a product and using ABC to cost a product?

_____

_____

_____

AS-10 `LO 3`

Define activity cost pools.

_____

_____

_____

AS-11 LO 2

What is activity-based management?

_____

_____

AS-12 LO 4

What is a just in time inventory management system?

_____

_____

AS-13 LO 4

Provide examples of businesses that may use the JIT system.

_____

_____

_____

AS-14 LO 4

What is a pull strategy?

_____

_____

_____

AS-15 LO 4

Provide three advantages of the pull strategy.

_____

_____

_____

AS-16 LO 4

Provide three disadvantages of the pull strategy.

_____

_____

_____

AS-17 LO 5

What is lean manufacturing?

_____

_____

_____

AS-18 LO 5

Based on the lean manufacturing strategy, what is considered as a waste area?

_____

_____

_____

AS-19 LO 5

What are the seven areas of waste according to lean manufacturing?

_____

_____

AS-20 LO 6

What are the four types of costs included in the total cost of quality?

_____

_____

_____

AS-21 LO 6

Define prevention costs.

_____

_____

_____

AS-22 LO 6

What are appraisal costs?

_____

_____

_____

AS-23 LO 6

What is considered as an internal failure?

_____

_____

_____

AS-24 LO 6

Provide two examples of internal failure costs.

_____

_____

AS-25 `LO 6`

Provide two examples of external failure costs.

_____

_____

_____

AS-26 `LO 6`

Define total quality management (TQM).

_____

_____

AS-27 `LO 6`

Why might a business decide not to implement the TQM program?

_____

_____

_____

AS-28 `LO 6`

Explain the theory of constraints.

_____

_____

_____

AS-29 `LO 6`

What is a bottleneck?

_____

_____

_____

AS-30 `LO 6`

What is an internal constraint?

_____

_____

_____

AS-31 `LO 6`

Provide three examples of internal constraints.

_____

_____

AS-32 LO 6

What is an external constraint?

_____

_____

_____

AS-33 LO 6

Describe the TOC process.

_____

_____

_____

_____

_____

Application Questions Group A

AP-1A LO 3

To determine product costs, Cracker Oat uses activity-based costing. Match the appropriate factory overhead cost pools listed in column A to the activity base found in column B.

Column A-Overhead Cost Pool	Column B-Activity Base
1) Customer return processing	a) Kilowatt-hours used
2) Billing and collecting	b) Number of customer returns
3) Electricity	c) Number of customer purchase orders
4) Production set-ups	d) Number of set-ups

AP-2A LO 3

Last year, Walk The Walk Corporation (WTW) launched its new woman's footwear line, called Happy Feet. Happy Feet became a huge success that year. The company is considering manufacturing both a men's and a children's version of this particular line. WTW uses activity-based costing to determine its product costs. In WTW's case, the three activities required to manufacture footwear are separated into three departments (cutting, machining and finishing). The following table outlines the budgeted manufacturing overhead costs and the estimated direct labor hours for each production department for this year:

	Budgeted Manufacturing Overhead Costs (in $)	Estimated Direct Labor Hours
Cutting Department Overhead	130,000	8,600
Machining Department Overhead	200,000	10,000
Finishing Department Overhead	98,000	8,000
Total	428,000	26,600

The company uses direct labor hours to allocate production department overhead to the products. The following table identifies the direct labor hours required to make one unit (pair) for each product for each production department.

	Cutting Department Overhead	Machining Department Overhead	Finishing Department Overhead
Women	0.5	0.20	0.47
Men	0.52	0.21	0.44
Children	0.32	0.19	0.38

Required

a) Determine the budgeted overhead rates for each department. Round your answers to two decimal points.

b) Determine the manufacturing overhead per unit for each product.

_____

_____

_____

_____

_____

_____

AP-3A LO 3

Jackson Consulting Company offers consulting services to large retail firms. The company charges clients for direct consulting time and support services. The direct consulting time is based on the individual consultant's hourly rate, and the support service fees cost the client an additional $50 for each hour a consultant worked with the client. The firm currently employs three consultants: Joe Smith, Betsy Henderson and Peter Martin. Each consultant has a different charge-out rate. Joe charges $110 per hour, Betsy bills clients at $200 per hour, and Peter charges $400 per hour.

Jackson Consulting is about to bill three clients: Goldview, Mountaincrest and Mackdale. The following table indicates the amount of hours that the consultants have spent on each client.

	Joe Smith	Betsy Henderson	Peter Martin
Goldview	95	52	47
Mountaincrest	40	102	68
Mackdale	-	50	110

How much should Jackson Consulting bill Goldview, Mountaincrest and Mackdale?

_____

_____

_____

_____

_____

_____

_____

_____

_____

_____

_____

_____

_____

_____

AP-4A LO 3

The Uniform Clothing Company manufactures school uniforms. Management would like information on the profitability of each individual product line (pants, dress shirts, cardigans and skirts). The company has provided financial information regarding the four products and the activities involved in the manufacturing process.

	Pants	Dress Shirts	Cardigans	Skirts	
Revenue	$300,000	$498,000	$120,000	$210,000	1,128,000
Direct Costs	$200,000	$370,000	$99,000	$165,000	834,000
Number of Labor Hours	1,250	1,500	2,000	1,300	6,050
Number of Machine Hours	1,700	1,900	2,000	1,760	7,360
Items Sold	100,000	155,000	95,000	45,000	395,000

The company's overhead costs and cost allocation bases are indicated in the following table.

Activity	Total Costs	Cost Allocation Base
Production	$71,000	Number of machine hours
Finishing	130,000	Number of labor hours
Customer Support	90,000	Number of items sold

Assume the company uses an ABC system to allocate support costs to the four product lines. Calculate the operating income for each product line.

_____

_____

_____

_____

_____

_____

_____

_____

_____

_____

_____

_____

_____

AP-5A LO 3

Gorn Dominion Bank (GD) uses the ABC system to determine the costs to operate its checking and savings accounts. The bank has three activities that support these product lines: processing, customer support and database maintenance.

The activity allocation rates for 2019 are as follows:

Activity	Allocation Base	Cost per Allocation base
Processing	Number of transactions	$0.10 per transaction
Customer support	Number of calls	$9.00 per call
Database maintenance	Number of queries	$1.20 per query

The budgeted data for 2019 are as follows:

	Checking	Savings
Transactions per account	300	180
Number of calls per account	3	5
Number of queries per account	50	30

GD expects to open 4,500 checking accounts and 3,000 savings accounts in 2019.

Required

a) Determine the total budgeted cost for 2019.

_____

_____

_____

_____

b) Calculate the total budgeted annual support costs per checking account.

_____

_____

c) Calculate the total annual support costs per savings account.

_____

_____

AP-6A LO 3

The Great Fone Company designs and manufactures cell phones. The company currently offers two models; the T340 and the SS360. The company has three operating departments: design, engineering and production. In the past, the company has been allocating the manufacturing overhead based on machine hours. However, Laura Simmie, the product manager of T340, has a hunch that the current method of using only machine hours as a cost allocation base is resulting in the allocation of too much overhead costs to the product. She has proposed that the company use the ABC system to cost products.

In 2019, the actual manufacturing overhead was $200,000. The following indicates the total amount of machine hours used for the production of each cell phone model in 2019.

	Machine Hours
T340	2,000 hours
SS360	2,000 hours
Total machine hours	4,000 hours

Required

a) Calculate the manufacturing overhead cost allocation rate using machine hours.

_____

_____

b) Determine the manufacturing overhead allocated to each model using the manufacturing overhead cost allocation rate determined in part a).

_____

_____

c) The Great Fone Company is considering changing its costing system by tracing manufacturing overhead costs to the three operating activities. The following is the amount of manufacturing overhead costs traceable to the designing, engineering and production activities.

Operating Areas	Cost Drivers	Total Costs
Designing	Number of design hours	$80,000
Engineering	Number of engineering hours	40,000
Production	Number of machine hours	80,000
Total		$200,000

The total cost allocation units used for each product line are:

Cost Allocation Base	T340	SS360	Total
Design hours	1,100	1,400	2,500
Engineering hours	1,700	1,800	3,500
Machine Hours	2,000	2,000	4,000

Determine the manufacturing overhead rate for each activity. In addition, use the manufacturing overhead rates to calculate the allocated overhead for each model.

_____

_____

_____

_____

_____

_____

_____

d) Was Laura's 'hunch' well founded?

_____

_____

_____

_____

_____

_____

_____

_____

_____

AP-7A `LO` `4`

Quatra Company manufactures vacuum bags and uses the JIT system. The following shows last year's demand for each quarter:

Q1	50,000 bags
Q2	65,000 bags
Q3	35,000 bags
Q4	25,000 bags

Each vacuum bag requires 130 grams of material. On average, the material costs the company $1 per 100 grams. Assume vacuum bags are delivered to customers at the end of each quarter.

Assume materials are purchased based on the JIT system. Determine how much Quatra spent on materials for each quarter.

AP-8A `LO` `5`

Hugen Smucks Pizza Palace makes fresh pizzas every day. Although the demand is normally 25 pizzas per day, Hugen Smucks often produces more than double the amount. Hugen Smucks also has a policy of delivering pizzas within 40 minutes. If Hugen Smucks fails to deliver within that time frame, the pizza will be free of charge. Many of its customers live 20 km away and are located in high traffic areas. Instead of taking toll roads that costs, on average, $1 per one-way trip to avoid the traffic, the company often delivers the pizzas late.

How can Hugen Smucks improve their operations? Consider discussing the applicable areas of waste from lean manufacturing.

AP-9A LO 6

ABT Company reports the following expenditures:

Design Reviews	$15,000
Employee Training Programs	2,000
Inspection and Tests	6,400
Storage Costs	20,000
In-house Scrap and Rework	5,000
Customer Return	6,500

Required

a) How much did ABT Company spend on preventing errors?

b) How much did the company invest in evaluating quality before the product is sent to customers?

c) Determine the amount of money spent on internal failures.

d) What was the total cost attributable to external failures?

e) Determine total quality costs.

Application Questions Group B

AP-1B LO 3

Berco Manufacturing budgeted to work 40,000 direct labor hours in the upcoming period. The company uses a single overhead rate based on direct labor hours. The following is the company's factory budgeted overhead costs:

Plant Building Depreciation	$600,000
Utilities	80,000
Maintenance	120,000

If a product requires 20 direct labor hours per unit, what is the overhead cost per unit associated with it?

_____

_____

_____

_____

AP-2B LO 3

Auto Moto Company manufactures car parts. The company performs five activities to produce the Tek Engine, the SanKo Muffler and the Spectra Carburetor. The activity rates for each activity are as follows:

Activity	Activity Rate
Design	$22 per design hour
Engineering	$30 per engineering hour
Production	$10 per machine hour
Assembly	$11 per direct manufacturing labor hour
Inspecting	$17 per inspection

Auto Moto estimated the amount of activity to be used by the three products for month of June. The estimated activity-base usage quantities and units produced are provided in the table below.

	Tek Engine	SanKo Muffler	Spectra Carburetor
Design Hours	14,000	9,000	8,700
Engineering Hours	22,000	12,000	5,000
Machine Hours	120,000	90,000	70,000
Direct Manufacturing Labor Hours	150,000	110,000	32,000
Number of Inspections	180	150	180
Units Produced	70,000	140,000	180,000

Required

a)   Calculate the overhead costs allocated to the Tek Engines and the overhead cost per unit.

_____

_____

_____

_____

_____

_____

_____

_____

_____

b)   Calculate the overhead costs allocated to the SanKo Muffler and the overhead cost per unit.

_____

_____

_____

_____

c)   Calculate the overhead costs allocated to the Spectra Carburetor and the overhead cost per unit.

_____

_____

_____

_____

AP-3B LO 3

AirBo Manufacturing uses activity-based costing for its jet engine process. AirBo separates manufacturing overhead into three activities: materials handling, assembly and inspection. The following is the budgeted cost for each manufacturing activity and their cost allocation bases:

	Materials Handling	Assembly	Inspection
Total Budgeted Cost	$900,000	$300,000	$280,000
Cost Allocation Base	Number of parts	Number of direct labor hours	Number of inspections

These jet engines are expected to consume 7,000 parts, require 4,000 direct labor hours and 175 inspections. Suppose AirBo builds two types of engines (Engine A and Engine B). During the month, engine A consumed 3,000 parts, required 2,000 direct labor hours and required 80 inspections. Engine B consumed 4,000 parts, required 2,000 direct labor hours and required 95 inspections. During the month, the company manufactured 11 type A engines and 9 type B engines.

Required

a)　For each manufacturing activity, calculate the activity rate.

_____

_____

_____

_____

b)　Determine the manufacturing overhead unit cost for each type of engine.

_____

_____

_____

_____

AP-4B LO 3

Joe Kologo identified the following cost pools and cost allocation bases:

Cost pools	Budgeted Costs	Cost Allocation base
Electric power	$120	60 kilowatt hours
Material handling	300	50 lbs of material
Machine setup	120	5 setup hours

Joe provides the following information regarding the monthly production of J300 and K500:

	J300	K500
Direct materials costs	$60	$45
Direct manufacturing labor costs	$10	$20
Number of setup hours	20	35
Kilowatt hours	5	2
Pounds of material	20	30
Number of units produced	20	15

Calculate the unit cost for J300 and K500.

_____
_____
_____
_____
_____
_____
_____
_____
_____
_____
_____
_____
_____
_____
_____
_____
_____
_____
_____
_____
_____
_____

AP-5B LO 3

One Stop Convenience Inc. (OSC) provides the following store overhead costs for 2019:

Activity	Cost Allocation Base	Cost per Unit of Allocation Base
Purchase orders	2,000 orders	$15 per order
Shelf-stocking	3,000 stocking hours	$10 per stocking hour
Delivering	7,000 deliveries	$19 per delivery

The following shows the total amount of resources required by Trisk and Volt (soft drinks).

	Purchase Orders	Stocking Hours	Deliveries
Trisk	1,100 orders	1,200 hours	3,500 deliveries
Volt	900 orders	1,800 hours	3,500 deliveries

Assume OSC expects to sell 50,000 bottles of Trisk and 70,000 bottles of Volt. Calculate the overhead cost per unit of each soft drink.

_____

_____

_____

_____

_____

_____

_____

_____

_____

_____

_____

AP-6B LO 3

Kerox Company manufactures two types of laser printers: monochrome and multifunction. Currently, manufacturing overhead is allocated based solely on the consumption of direct labor hours. For the upcoming quarter, the company expects to produce 2,000 units of monochrome printers and 1,300 units of multifunction printers, and expects manufacturing overhead costs to be $25,000. Each monochrome and multifunction laser printer requires 0.5 direct labor hours and 0.7 direct labor hours, respectively.

The following table outlines the selling price, material and labor cost for each unit of monochrome and multifunction laser printers manufactured.

	Selling Price	Direct Material	Direct Labor
Monochrome	$110	$20	$5
Multifunction	$395	$80	$22

The company is considering changing its current costing system to the ABC costing system. If it decides to use this method, it would separate the manufacturing support costs into three activities: handling purchase orders, inspecting and setting up production flow. The budgeted manufacturing overhead cost for purchase orders, inspections and product setups are $10,000, $6,000 and $9,000, respectively. The following table indicates the cost allocation usage for each product.

	Monochrome	Multifunction
Number of purchase orders	70	110
Number of inspections	50	250
Number of setups	75	375

Required

a) For each product, calculate the manufacturing cost per unit under the current costing system (using direct labor hours to allocate manufacturing overhead).

_____

_____

_____

_____

_____

_____

_____

_____

_____

_____

b) For each product, calculate the manufacturing cost per unit under the ABC costing system.

_____

_____

_____

_____

_____

_____

_____

_____

_____

_____

_____

_____

_____

_____

_____

_____

_____

_____

_____

_____

_____

_____

_____

_____

_____

_____

_____

AP-7B LO 4

Identify which the following statements are advantages of the JIT inventory system.

a) Reduces or eliminates overproduction, since products are manufactured only when required by a customer.

b) Exposed to volatile price fluctuations of raw material.

c) Business is still able to operate if suppliers are unable to deliver raw material on time.

d) By stockpiling raw material and partially completed inventory, problems in one department may not immediately affect the subsequent department.

e) Encourages having better relationships with suppliers to ensure raw materials are delivered on time and are of good quality.

_____

_____

_____

_____

AP-8B LO 6

GetFit Limited manufactures dumbbells. Identify the following list of costs and activities as prevention (P), appraisal (A), internal failure (IF), external failure (EF) or other business costs (O).

	Warranty Claims
	Salary of Inspection Supervisor
	Scrap
	Product Recalls
	Equipment Depreciation
	Excess Inventory
	Quality Assurance Training

AP-9B LO 4 5 6

Match the terms in column A with the correct definition in column B.

Column A		Column B
A. Just-in-time (JIT) system		A management concept that focuses on continuously reducing errors and satisfying customers.
B. Lean Manufacturing		A stage in a process that slows down or stops the entire operation.
C. Total Quality Management		A manufacturing strategy that seeks high level of production with minimal inventory balance while eliminating costs that do not produce value.
D. Bottleneck		Inventory management system which minimizes the amount of inventory kept in stock.

Critical Thinking

CT-1 LO 6

Jolly Goods Limited specializes in hand-made Christmas ornaments. These ornaments go through three processes: cutting, assembling and finishing. Two days ago, the company received an unexpected order for 2,000 ornaments. Both the cutting and assembling departments have the capacity to fulfill the order and would have to work at 100% capacity to complete it. Due to the amount of detailed work required to produce each ornament, the finishing department does not have enough time to meet the deadline. The company as a whole is working at 85% of capacity. As a result, the company is concerned that it will be unable to accept the order.

Identify the constraint and recommend a possible solution for Jolly Goods Limited.

Chapter 5

COST-VOLUME-PROFIT ANALYSIS

LEARNING OBJECTIVES

LO 1   Classify costs into variable costs, fixed costs and mixed costs

LO 2   Separate mixed costs into fixed and variable costs

LO 3   Calculate and analyze contribution margin and contribution margin ratio

LO 4   Perform breakeven analysis and target analysis

LO 5   Perform sensitivity analysis

LO 6   Apply CVP analysis to a multi-product company

LO 7   Calculate degree of operating leverage and margin of safety

LO 8   Describe ethics relating to CVP analysis

AMEENGAGE   *Access **ameengage.com** for integrated resources including tutorials, practice exercises, the digital textbook and more.*

———— Assessment Questions ————

AS-1 LO 1

What are variable costs?

_____

_____

AS-2 LO 1

Identify the relationship between variable costs and volume of production.

_____

_____

_____

AS-3 LO 1

Define fixed costs.

_____

_____

AS-4 LO 1

Identify the relationship, if any, between fixed costs and volume of production.

_____

_____

AS-5 LO 1

Is it true that fixed costs never change?

_____

_____

AS-6 LO 1

What is a step fixed cost?

_____

_____

_____

AS-7 LO 1

Provide an example of a step fixed cost.

_____

_____

_____

AS-8 LO 1

Which type of product cost is often a step variable cost in terms of its actual cost behavior and why?

_____

_____

_____

AS-9 LO 1

What is a difference between the relevant ranges for step fixed costs and step variable costs?

_____

_____

AS-10 LO 2

What are mixed costs?

_____

_____

AS-11 LO 2

What is an advantage of using the high-low method to separate mixed costs?

_____

_____

AS-12 LO 2

What is the major drawback of using the high-low method to separate mixed costs into the variable and fixed portions?

_____

_____

_____

AS-13 LO 2

What is an advantage of using the least-square regression method instead of the high-low method to separate mixed costs?

_____

_____

_____

_____

AS-14 LO 1

Briefly define cost behavior.

_____

_____

AS-15 LO 3

How is contribution margin calculated?

_____

_____

AS-16 LO 3

What does the contribution margin represent?

_____

_____

AS-17 LO 3

What is the difference between a contribution margin income statement and a formal income statement?

_____

_____

_____

AS-18 `LO` `4`

Explain how the breakeven point (in units) can be determined using the graphical method.

_____

_____

_____

AS-19 `LO` `4`

Describe how the breakeven point (in units) can be determined if the equation method is used.

_____

_____

_____

AS-20 `LO` `4`

How can managers use the equation method to calculate the volume needed to yield a particular operating profit?

_____

_____

_____

AS-21 `LO` `4`

How do managerial accountants benefit from cost-volume-profit (CVP) analysis?

_____

_____

_____

AS-22 `LO` `3`

How is the contribution margin ratio (CM ratio) calculated?

_____

_____

_____

AS-23 `LO` `3`

What information does the CM ratio represent? Describe one of the uses of the CM ratio.

_____

_____

_____

AS-24 LO 5

Briefly describe differential analysis.

_____

_____

AS-25 LO 7

What does the margin of safety represent?

_____

_____

AS-26 LO 7

Explain how the margin of safety is related to the riskiness of a business.

_____

_____

_____

AS-27 LO 6

What does sales mix refer to in a business?

_____

_____

AS-28 LO 6

When is it appropriate to use a weighted-average contribution margin?

_____

_____

_____

AS-29 LO 6

Provide the formula used to calculate the weighted-average contribution margin for a company that produces and sells two types of products.

_____

_____

_____

AS-30 LO 5

What is sensitivity analysis?

_____

_____

AS-31 [LO 5]

How does performing a sensitivity analysis assist managers in making decisions?

_____

_____

_____

AS-32 [LO 7]

Define operating leverage.

_____

_____

AS-33 [LO 7]

How is the degree of operating leverage calculated? What does it mean?

_____

_____

_____

AS-34 [LO 8]

What are some problems that may result from a manager incorrectly classifying a mixed cost due to a lack of technical competence?

_____

_____

_____

_____

Application Questions Group A

AP-1A LO 1

The Toys Store (TTS) sells stuffed animals, toys and board games. It has a total fixed cost of $30,000 per year. Due to limited space, TTS can only fit 50,000 items in the store. Once it exceeds 50,000 units, TTS will have to rent a storage room at a fixed cost of $10,000 a year. The storage room can only store a maximum of 40,000 items.

Illustrate the above scenario in the graph shown below.

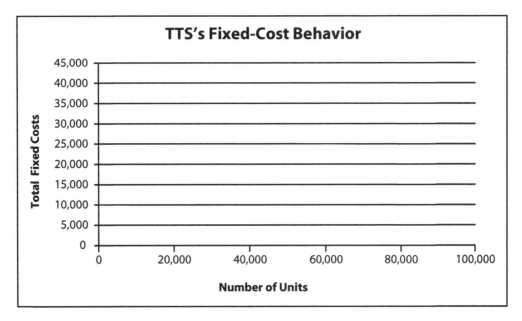

AP-2A LO 2

Bike Attire Inc. is a manufacturer of bicycle tires. The cost of electricity is considered a mixed cost by the company. The variable portion of the electricity cost is assumed to be dependant on the number of units produced. The following is the related cost and activity data for the past six months:

Month	Volume of Production (number of units)	Cost of Electricity
July	70,000	$6,000
August	45,000	$4,500
September	35,000	$3,800
October	25,000	$3,400
November	32,000	$3,700
December	60,000	$5,200

Required

a) Using the high-low method, factor out the fixed and variable portions of the electricity cost.

_____

_____

_____

_____

_____

b) Assume that the company used the least-square regression method to separate the fixed and variable portions of the electricity cost instead. The calculated formula was y = 0.079x + 1,842. What are the fixed and variable portions in this case?

_____

_____

_____

AP-3A LO 2

At Stark Medical Centre, the cost of X-rays has a fixed component and a variable component related to the number of X-rays taken. The cost and number of X-rays taken at the medical centre for the past seven months are provided below.

Month	Number of X-Rays Taken	Cost of X-Rays
June	650	$2,700
July	700	$2,850
August	500	$2,250
September	420	$1,750
October	460	$2,000
November	300	$1,270
December	350	$1,500

Required

a) Using the high-low method, determine a formula for calculating X-ray costs in a given month.

_____

_____

_____

_____

_____

_____

b) What would be the expected X-ray cost incurred for a month in which 585 X-rays are taken?

_____

_____

_____

_____

AP-4A LO 4

Laura Lopez sells carpets for $600 each. She purchases each carpet for $300 and spends $50,000 for fixed costs.

Required

a) Calculate operating income if Laura sells 200 carpets.

b) Calculate the revenues needed to obtain an operating income of $40,000.

AP-5A LO 4

The Crazy Hair Salon provides special-occasion haircuts and generates average revenue of $50 per customer. The salon's fixed costs are $40,000 per year, which include rent, utilities and magazine subscriptions. Its variable costs are $20 per customer. Target operating income for the year is $90,000.

Required

a) Calculate the revenues needed to obtain the target operating income.

b) How many haircuts have to be provided to earn an operating income of $80,000? To breakeven?

c) Calculate the operating income if 6,000 haircuts are provided.

AP-6A LO 4

The manager of Bottle Up Ltd. graphed the relationship between the company's operating income and the number of water bottles produced and sold.

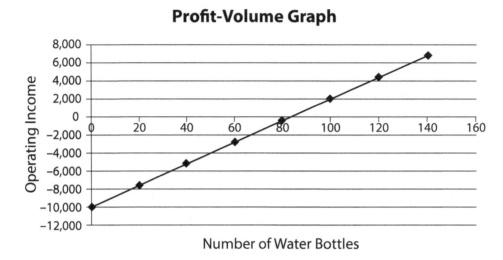

Profit-Volume Graph

Required

a) Locate and highlight the breakeven point (in units).
b) Locate and highlight the number of units required to achieve an operating income of $2,000.

AP-7A LO 3 4

El Jardin Entertainment offers theater packages at $50 per unit. The package includes snacks, beverages and a ticket. The costs incurred by the program are as follows:

Variable Costs	$20 per package
Fixed Expenses	$20,000

Required

a) Calculate the contribution margin per package.

_____

_____

_____

_____

b) Determine the breakeven point in units (packages).

_____

_____

_____

_____

_____

_____

c) If the theater can accommodate only 500 individuals, how much should El Jardin Entertainment charge per package to break even? Assume that variable and fixed costs remain the same.

_____

_____

_____

_____

_____

d) Using the information from part (c), how much should El Jardin charge as an entrance fee if they want to have an operating income of $1,000?

_____

_____

_____

AP-8A LO 3

In the following chart, fill in the missing cells for each of the following independent scenarios. Perform your calculations on the next page.

Scenario	Revenue	Variable Costs	Fixed Costs	Total Costs	Operating Income	CM Ratio	Contribution Margin
1	$500		$400	$600	($100)		
2	2,100			1,300		76.19%	
3		710		1,110	990		
4	800		540		(110)		430

Calculations

_____

_____

_____

_____

_____

_____

_____

_____

_____

_____

_____

_____

_____

_____

_____

_____

AP-9A LO 4

Xander buys and sells ladies' handbags. The average selling price is $480 per bag. Average variable costs (purchase price of bags plus freight costs and selling expenses) amounts to $250 per bag. Xander's fixed costs equal $1,800,000 per year.

Required

For each year, calculate the number of units needed to:

a) break even.

b) earn $250,000 operating income.

c) earn an operating income equal to 25% of total sales.

AP-10A LO 4 5 7

BGB Tuna Processing manufactures and sells canned tuna. Variable cost per can amounts to $11 and the selling price of each can is $24. Total annual fixed costs amount to $9,600,000. Sales are estimated to amount to 1,200,000 cans of tuna.

Required

a) If the company sells according to their estimates, what is the degree of operating leverage?

b) How many cans of tuna does the company need to sell in order to break even?

c) If the company increases the sales volume (cans) by 25%, how much will operating income increase in dollars? In percentage change? Use the degree of operating leverage.

d) If the company spends $30,000 as additional advertising expense (fixed cost), sales volume will increase by 10%. Determine the new degree of operating leverage and the new breakeven point in units.

_____

_____

_____

_____

_____

_____

_____

_____

_____

_____

_____

AP-11A LO 5

Oh My Bagel Co. operates four bagel stores in New York. The owner has provided the following budgeted data for next year.

Revenue	$11,450,000
Fixed Costs	3,185,000
Variable Costs (depends on the # of bagels sold)	7,700,000

Required

For each scenario, determine the dollar impact on Oh My Bagel's:
   a) Revenue
   b) Variable Costs
   c) Fixed Costs
   d) Contribution Margin
   e) Budgeted Operating Income

Consider each scenario independently.

i. A 5% increase in fixed costs.

_____

_____

_____

_____

_____

_____

_____

_____

_____

_____

ii. A 10% increase in contribution margin, but holding revenue constant.

_____

_____

_____

_____

_____

_____

_____

_____

_____

_____

iii. A 15% increase in fixed costs and 10% increase in units sold.

_____

_____

_____

_____

_____

_____

_____

_____

_____

_____

_____

AP-12A LO 7

The Kandy Shop has an operating income of $20,000.

a) Calculate the degree of operating leverage for each of the independent cases (assuming operating income is held constant):

i.   Contribution Margin is $50,000.
ii. CM ratio is 50% and revenue is $136,000.
iii. Selling price per unit is $30, variable costs per unit are $20 and it sold 4,000 units.

_____

_____

_____

_____

_____

_____

_____

_____

b)   State the scenario with the highest degree of operating leverage. What does this mean?

_____

_____

_____

AP-13A LO 4 5

ToTomato is holding a four-day sale at Fresh Foodilicious, a local food market. ToTomato plans to sell tomatoes at $0.75 each. ToTomato will have fixed costs of $80 (related to the tomato purchase agreement) and total variable costs of $0.20 per tomato sold and produced. ToTomato will incur an additional cost for using the store space during the sale. Fresh Foodilicious has offered ToTomato two payment alternatives for the use of space:

1)   fixed payment of $120.
2)   10% of total revenue earned during the four-day sale.

Required

a)   For each option, determine how many tomatoes ToTomato needs to produce and sell in order to break even.

_____

_____

_____

_____

_____

_____

_____

_____

b)   At what level of production volume will both options yield the same operating income?

_____

_____

_____

_____

_____

_____

_____

_____

_____

_____

_____

AP-14A LO 5 7

Mr. Duster wants to open a new vacuum store called the Dust-Off in a nearby plaza. Mr. Duster will be selling vacuums for $150 each. Variable costs (not including the leasing costs below) are $95 for every vacuum.

In terms of lease payments, the plaza has provided him with three options:

    i.   Pay $25 per vacuum sold
    ii. $20,000 per month
    iii. $15,000 per month and $10 per vacuum sold

Required

a) Calculate the monthly operating income for each of the three options if 300 units are sold and if 700 units are sold.

b) At a production level of 700 units, which option should be recommended?

c) Calculate the degree of operating leverage for the second lease option if Mr. Duster sells 700 vacuums.

AP-15A LO 3 5

Complex Keys Ltd. is a manufacturer of computer keyboards. It is now December 1, 2019. The company's contribution margin statement for November 2019 is presented below. During November, 5,000 units were sold.

Complex Keys Contribution Margin Statement November 2019	
Sales	$150,000
Less Variable Costs	81,000
Contribution Margin	69,000
Less Fixed Costs	
Rent	21,000
Operating Income	$48,000

Complex Keys is now faced with a decision to expand its operations by renting more space to increase production. If the expansion takes place, sales volume will increase by 500 units per month. The extra rent will cost $8,000/month.

Required

a) Recreate the entire contribution margin. Should Complex Keys proceed with the expansion?

Complex Keys Monthly Contribution Margin Statement	
Sales	
Less Variable Costs	
Contribution Margin	
Less Fixed Costs:	
Rent	
Operating Income	

b) What is the contribution margin ratio (based on the original contribution margin statement)?

c) Using incremental analysis, explain why Complex Keys should or should not proceed with the expansion.

AP-16A LO 6

Sushi Sushi Restaurant offers two types of all-you-can eat options: regular and ultimate. Ultimate provides more choices than the regular menu. The restaurant incurs fixed costs of $10,000 per month. Its planned sales mix in units is 30% regular and 70% ultimate. The following table indicates the selling price and variable costs for each option:

	Regular	**Ultimate**
Selling Price:	$17	$21
Variable Cost:	10	13

How many units of each of the regular and ultimate options need to be sold each month for the company to break even, assuming the planned sales mix is maintained.

AP-17A LO 6

Jim Slugger Inc. manufactures only two products: wooden baseball bats and titanium baseball bats. The company has provided the following financial information for the past year:

Product	Contribution Margin per Unit	Sales Quantity
Titanium bat	$11	40,000 units
Wooden bat	$13	60,000 units

Total fixed costs for the year amounted to $1,100,000.

Required

a) Calculate the weighted-average contribution margin per unit.

b) Assuming the past year's sales mix is maintained, how many titanium bats and wooden bats have to be sold during the year in order to break even?

_____

_____

_____

_____

_____

c) Prove that selling 84,636 titanium bats and 13,000 wooden bats is approximately another combination of break even quantities.

_____

_____

_____

_____

Application Questions Group B

AP-1B LO **1**

Chai Electronics distributes satellite radios. The company purchases the radios from a supplier at a cost of $70 per unit. It pays $5,000 per month to rent a storage room, which can hold up to 1,000 radios. Prepare a graph to illustrate total costs for the range between 0–1,000 units.

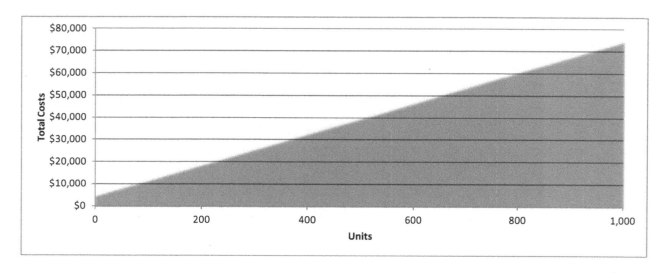

Analysis

If Chai Electronics were to be profitable, and if it were to plot the sales revenue line on the same chart, would the sales revenue line be more or less steep than the total cost line?

AP-2B LO 2

Port Colborne Company (PCC) manufactures a single product. The following table reports production information for the last 12 months.

Month	Units Made	Total Manufacturing Cost
1	800	$4,000
2	1,200	$8,000
3	2,000	$12,000
4	2,600	$10,000
5	3,000	$9,000
6	2,800	$11,000
7	4,200	$12,400
8	4,600	$10,000
9	4,200	$15,400
10	4,700	$15,600
11	3,600	$11,800
12	5,000	$16,000

Required

a) Plot the relationship between units made (on the horizontal axis) and total manufacturing cost (on the vertical axis).

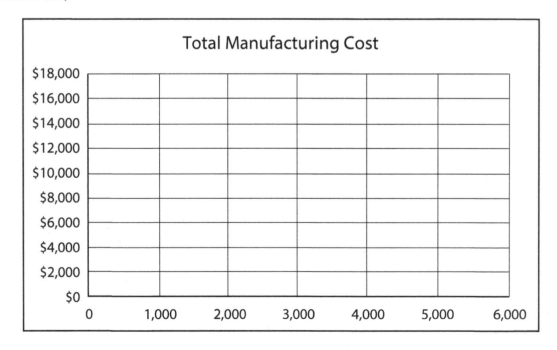

b) Estimate the cost function using the high-low method.

_____

_____

_____

_____

c) The accountant at PCC does not believe that the high-low method provides a reasonable cost estimate and has proposed using the results in months 4 and 11 to estimate the cost function. Prepare the estimate of the cost function using these two observations.

_____

_____

_____

_____

AP-3B LO 2

Mackey Publishing Company (Mackey) publishes novels. The monthly equipment maintenance cost for Mackey is considered to be a mixed cost. The variable portion of the cost is related to the number of novels published. The production volume and maintenance costs for the past six months are presented below. Mackey uses the high-low method to separate mixed costs into its fixed and variable portions.

Month	Volume of Production (Number of Novels)	Equipment Maintenance Costs
January	300,000	$4,500
February	450,000	$6,800
March	150,000	$3,800
April	80,000	$2,900
May	480,000	$7,600
June	250,000	$4,100

Required

a) Calculate the variable rate for the equipment maintenance cost. Do not round your answer.

_____

_____

_____

_____

_____

b) Calculate the fixed portion of the equipment maintenance cost.

_____

_____

_____

c) Assume that 420,000 novels is the budgeted production level for July. Using the results of the high-low method in parts a) and b), what is the expected total equipment maintenance cost for July?

_____

_____

_____

_____

_____

AP-4B LO 3 4

Frog Company (FC) manufactures ceramic frogs that are used for lawn decorations. Each frog sells for $25 and has variable manufacturing costs of $11. Fixed costs at FC amount to $2,300,000.

Required

a) Calculate contribution margin per unit and contribution margin ratio.

_____

_____

b) If FC wishes to earn $350,000, how many frog ornaments must it sell?

_____

_____

AP-5B LO 4

District Distribution (DD) delivers advertising flyers to homes. DD is paid $0.05 for each flyer it delivers. Employees are paid $0.03 for each flyer delivered. There are no other variable costs. Fixed costs at DD amount to $125,000 per year.

How many flyers must DD deliver to earn an operating profit of $75,000?

_____

_____

_____

_____

AP-6B LO 4

Lighten Up Company manufactures and sells color-adjusting light bulbs. For its 2019 business plan, Lighten Up made the following financial estimates:

Selling Price	$1/unit
Variable Costs	$0.50/unit
Annual Fixed Costs	$5,000

Required

a) Using the graphical method, first determine the number of light bulbs needed to break even and then determine the volume needed to yield an operating income of $5,000.

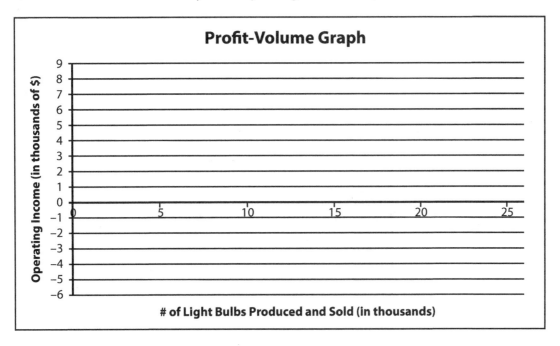

b) Repeat part a), but using the equation method.

AP-7B LO 3 4

Dumbledore Corporation forecasts that next year it can sell 25,000 units of its toaster ovens (for $1,000,000) in the open market. The expected contribution margin ratio is 45%. Fixed costs are estimated to be $375,000.

Required

a) What is the selling price per unit?

b) Calculate the contribution margin if 25,000 units are produced and sold.

c) Calculate the contribution margin per unit.

d) If the company decides to sell its products in the open market, determine the amount of units required to break even.

e) Determine the operating income if 25,000 units are produced and sold.

f) Determine the amount of revenue that needs to be generated to yield an operating income of $100,000.

AP-8B `LO 3`

In the following chart, fill in the missing cells for each of the following independent scenarios. Perform your calculations below the chart.

Scenario	Selling Price per Unit	Variable Costs per Unit	Total Units Sold	Contribution Margin	Fixed Cost	Operating Income (Loss)
1	$10	$5	400			$1,000
2		12	210	630	780	
3	24		330	1,320	2,000	
4	9	5		560		360

Calculations

_____

_____

_____

_____

_____

_____

_____

_____

_____

_____

_____

_____

_____

_____

_____

AP-9B `LO 3 4 5`

Gotta Go Green (GGG) manufactures and sells reusable grocery bags. GGG currently sells 1,200,000 bags per year at a selling price of $2 per unit. Variable costs amount to $0.95 per bag and total fixed costs amount to $1,000,000 per year.

Required

a) Determine the current operating income.

_____

_____

_____

b) Express contribution margin as a percentage of total sales. What is another term for this value and what does it imply?

_____

_____

_____

_____

c) Calculate the number of reusable grocery bags that have to be produced and sold to break even.

_____

_____

_____

_____

d) Calculate the number of units to yield an operating income of $300,000.

_____

_____

_____

e) Calculate the new break even point in units for each of the following changes:

i)   A 6% increase in fixed cost.

_____

_____

_____

_____

_____

_____

ii)   A 15% increase in selling price and a 10% increase in fixed cost.

_____

_____

_____

_____

_____

_____

_____

_____

_____

AP-10B LO 4 7

Deltech Speakers Inc. manufactures one type of computer speakers. The average selling price is $110 per speaker set. The average variable cost amounts to $60 per speaker set. The company's fixed costs are $45,000 per month.

Required

a) Calculate the monthly volume of sales needed to break even.

b) Determine the break even point in sales dollars.

c) If the company's current monthly sales amount is $120,000, what is the margin of safety in dollars and in units?

AP-11B LO 5

John's Bookkeeping and Tax Services (John's) provides bookkeeping services to small business and personal income tax returns. John's charges customers $50 per hour for any work done. John's has five employees. John's pays each employee $50,000 per year and each employee provides 2,000 hours of work per year. Other fixed costs at John's amount to $150,000 per year. John's expects to provide 9,500 hours of work to its customers in the upcoming year.

Required

Prepare an Excel spreadsheet similar to the one prepared for Othello Pizza to answer the following questions.

a) What is the expected operating profit in the base case scenario above?

b) John's believes that if the hourly rate is reduced to $46.00, demand will jump to 11,000 hours. However, variable cost will increase to $7.00 per hour because the employees will have to be paid overtime in addition to their fixed wage. What is the expected operating profit in this scenario?

c) John's is thinking of using a piece rate approach to compensation. Workers would be paid $150 for each job they complete. The average number of hours per job is 5. Therefore the total average variable cost per job will be $175 (150 plus 5*5 for other variable costs). John's feels that this will increase worker productivity. If the average price per job is set at $240 John's feels that the potential demand will be 2,600 jobs. However, the total number of jobs the five employees will be able to deliver, even though worker productivity is expected to increase in the piece rate system, is only 2,500. What is the expected operating profit in this scenario?

AP-12B LO 7

Manadaue Furniture manufactures specialized doors that cater to the needs of new residences and buildings in General Santos City. The contribution margin statement for the month of July is presented below:

Sales	$5,200,000
Variable Costs	2,950,000
Contribution Margin	2,250,000
Fixed Costs	1,800,000
Operating Income	**$450,000**

The supporting documents revealed that 25,000 units of doors were sold in July.

Required

a) Determine the company's degree of operating leverage.

b) What is the percentage change in operating income if the volume of sales next month will increase to 30,000 units? Utilize the degree of operating leverage in your answer.

_____

_____

_____

_____

c) If the sales volume increases to 30,000 units in August, how much operating income should the company expect?

_____

_____

_____

_____

_____

_____

AP-13B LO 4 5

Eastern Pottery Company (EPC) manufactures a single line of pottery cups that it customizes for its customers. Currently, sales are 500,000 units per year. Cups are sold for $12.00 and have a total variable cost of $8.00. EPC has capacity to produce up to 600,000 cups per year.

Required

a) The EPC marketing manager has proposed an advertising campaign that would cost $400,000. What is the minimum increase in unit sales that would justify this campaign?

_____

_____

_____

b) The EPC marketing manager believes that increasing the quality of the raw materials used to make the cups would allow EFC to increase sales. If total variable cost per cup was increased to $9.00 per cup and the current price of $12 per cup is maintained what would be the new level of unit sales that would justify this increase?

_____

_____

_____

_____

_____

_____

_____

c) The EPC production supervisor has proposed purchasing a new machine that she believes will reduce variable cost per unit and increase sales each year. With the new machine expected total unit sales would be 525,000 and the variable cost per unit for cups would be $7.80 cup. If the expected life of the new machine is 5 years, at what price of the new machine will the benefits of the new machine equal its costs?

_____

_____

_____

_____

AP-14B LO 5

Kangaroo Company (KC) is a holding company that owns various businesses. KC is thinking of purchasing an existing grocery store and is choosing amongst three alternatives: a discount grocery store, a grocery store that would compete with chain grocery stores, and a premium grocery store.

Research has gleaned the following information on the three alternatives:

	Discount Store	Conventional Store	Premium Store
Quarterly Fixed Costs	$7,500,000	$9,500,000	$12,500,000
Contribution Margin Ratio	43%	47%	55%
Projected Quarterly Sales	$19,000,000	$22,000,000	$24,000,000

The initial investment in each facility will be three times quarterly fixed costs. Based solely on financial considerations, which store type would you recommend?

	Discount Store	Conventional Store	Premium Store
Quarterly Fixed Costs			
Contribution Margin Ratio			
Projected Quarterly Sales			
Breakeven Revenue			
Quarterly Income			
Investment Required			
Return on Investment			

_____

_____

_____

_____

_____

_____

_____

_____

_____

AP-15B LO 5

Nashville Bat Company (NBC) produces a single line of wood baseball bats. NBC is considering purchasing a new lathe to produce the bats. The production manager is considering two alternative lathes. Lathe 1 will cost $1,000,000 will result in a variable cost per bat of $37.00. Lathe 2 will cost $700,000. Both lathes have a life expectancy of 3 years.

If annual bat sales are expected to be 500,000 units for the next 3 years what is the variable cost per bat using lathe 2 that will result, from a cost basis, in NBC being indifferent between the two machines?

_____

_____

_____

_____

_____

_____

_____

_____

_____

AP-16B LO 6

Selkirk Chemical Company (SCC) produces three glues that are used in commercial applications. The following information relates to the upcoming year.

	AQ36	B845	FX345	Total
Contribution per Gallon	$30,00	$24.00	$20.00	
Planned Sales (Gallons)	10,000	30,000	60,000	100,000
Fixed Costs				$2,000,000

Required

a) What is the expected Income associated with this plan?

	AQ36	B845	FX345	Total
Contribution per Gallon				
Planned Sales (Gallons)				
Fixed Costs				
Total Contribution Margin				
Income				

b) Assuming that the product mix remains constant what is the breakeven quantity of sales (in gallon) for each product?

	AQ36	B845	FX345	Total
Contribution per Gallon				
Planned Sales (Gallons)				
Mix				
Weighted Average Contribution Margin				
Fixed Costs				
Breakeven Sales*				

*Breakeven sales are rounded up.

c) Suppose that the SCC sales manager believes that while the product mix will remain constant total sales will be 110,000 litres. What will be the expected income at this level of sales?

	AQ36	B845	FX345	Total
Contribution Margin				
Mix				
Planned Sales				
Total Contribution Margin				
Fixed Costs				
Income				

Analysis

The sales manager at SCC now believes that while total sales will be 110,000 liters, the product mix will change as follows.

	AQ36	B845	FX345	Total
Contribution Margin	$30,00	$24.00	$20.00	
Mix	12%	32%	54%	

What is the expected income with this plan?

	AQ36	B845	FX345	Total
Contribution Margin				
Mix				
Planned Sales				
Total Contribution Margin				
Fixed Costs				
Income				

AP-17B LO 3 4 6

Ploy Media publishes and sells two magazines, including Rural Living and Urban Living. Its contribution margin income statement for July 2019 is as follows.

Ploy Media Contribution Margin Income Statement For the Month Ending July 31, 2019			
	Rural	**Urban**	**Total**
Sales	$400,000	$150,000	$550,000
Variable Costs	155,000	65,000	220,000
Contribution Margin	245,000	85,000	330,000
Fixed Costs			150,000
Operating Profit			$180,000

Required

a) Calculate the company-wide contribution margin ratio.

b) Calculate the company-wide breakeven point in sales dollars.

c) Prove that your answer in part b) is correct by using the sales figure from part b) to prepare a contribution margin income statement similar to the one above.

Critical Thinking

CT-1 LO 4 5

Vivian Lopez and Loren San will be opening a pastry store called Tasty Desserts. They are opening in two weeks and have still not decided how much to charge for their cakes and how much they should spend on advertisements and promotions.

The following information is available:

Tasty Dessert's variable costs per cake	$10
Tasty Dessert's fixed costs for the year	$12,500
Maximum production capacity for the year	5,000 cakes
Tasty Dessert's selling price per cake	?
Advertising budget	?
Competitor's selling price per cake (offer similar cakes as Tasty Dessert's)	$20

The two owners had the following discussion regarding the selling price and advertising budget:

Vivian: Opening day is in two weeks! Loren, we really need to figure out how much we'll be selling our cakes for and our advertising budget.

Loren: As a new store, I think we should charge the same rate as our competitors and advertise our store on the radio and local review blogs. I anticipate that these advertising expenses will increase our fixed costs by $3,000.

Vivian: Well, I think the best way to attract customers is to sell our cakes cheaper than anyone else. I'm thinking we should charge 10% lower than our competitor's rate. As for advertising, I don't think we need to spend money on advertisements at all. We can simply create a Facebook group and invite a bunch of friends and families. This way, we will generate more sales. In fact, I think we can potentially increase sales by 1,500 cakes.

Loren: I agree that we will probably sell more cakes if we charge 10% lower than our competitors. However, I don't think we will be able cover our fixed costs if we reduce our prices.
We should also be concerned with breaking even as quick as possible.

Whose suggested strategy should be recommended? Assume that 5,000 cakes will be sold.

Notes

Chapter 6

COSTING AND PRICING STRATEGIES

LEARNING OBJECTIVES

LO 1 Explain the differences between absorption costing and variable costing

LO 2 Prepare an income statement under absorption costing

LO 3 Prepare a contribution margin income statement under variable costing

LO 4 Identify the effect that the use of absorption costing or variable costing has on income from operations

LO 5 Calculate the selling price using the market based pricing and cost plus pricing methods and calculate the maximum allowable cost using the target costing method

LO 6 Identify ethical considerations related to costing and pricing

AMEENGAGE™ Access **ameengage.com** for integrated resources including tutorials, practice exercises, the digital textbook and more.

Assessment Questions

AS-1 LO 1

Explain the concept of absorption costing.

_____

_____

_____

AS-2 LO 1

What is variable costing?

_____

_____

_____

AS-3 LO 1

Explain how variable costing and absorption costing are used for financial reporting.

_____

_____

_____

_____

_____

AS-4 LO 1 4

Explain why absorption costing might show a different income from operations than the variable costing method.

_____

_____

_____

_____

_____

_____

_____

AS-5 LO 2

How are fixed manufacturing overhead expenses reported in the income statement under absorption costing?

_____

_____

_____

AS-6 LO 3

How are fixed manufacturing overhead expenses reported in the contribution margin income statement under variable costing?

_____

_____

_____

AS-7 LO 4

If the number of units manufactured is less than the number of units sold, which costing method (absorption or variable costing) would show a higher income from operations?

_____

_____

AS-8 LO 5

Explain the maximum profit pricing strategy.

_____

_____

_____

AS-9 LO 5

Define markup.

_____

_____

AS-10 LO 5

How does the cost plus pricing method determine a selling price?

_____

_____

AS-11 LO 5

Explain why a business might use the cost plus pricing method to determine a selling price.

_____

_____

_____

AS-12 LO 5

What is target costing?

_____

_____

_____

AS-13 LO 5

What are the advantages and disadvantages of using the target costing method?

_____

_____

_____

_____

AS-14 LO 6

How may a manager increase income from operations under absorption costing without increasing sales? Is doing so ethical? Explain.

_____

_____

_____

_____

_____

_____

_____

AS-15 LO 6

What ethical risks can a company encounter when it uses absorption costing?

_____

_____

_____

_____

_____

_____

_____

AS-16 LO 6

What is the impact of overproduction and how can it be avoided?

_____

_____

_____

_____

_____

_____

_____

_____

_____

_____

_____

_____

_____

_____

_____

_____

_____

_____

_____

Application Questions Group A

AP-1A LO 2 3

In 2019, Bran Sherry Inc. sold 50,000 units at a selling price of $35 per unit. The company manufactured 60,000 units. Variable manufacturing costs were $14 per unit manufactured. Fixed manufacturing costs amounted to $300,000. Variable marketing costs were $10 per unit sold, and the budgeted and actual fixed marketing costs were $40,000. Other fixed operating expenses amounted to $20,000. There was no beginning inventory.

Required

a) Calculate the company's 2019 income from operations using absorption costing.

b) Calculate the company's 2019 income from operations using variable costing.

_____

_____

_____

_____

_____

_____

_____

_____

_____

_____

_____

_____

_____

_____

_____

_____

_____

AP-2A LO 4

In 2019, a manufacturing company produced 200,000 units and sold 230,000 units. If the company's fixed manufacturing overhead rate was $25 per unit, which of the two costing methods (absorption and variable costing) will show a higher income from operations, and by how much?

_____

_____

_____

_____

_____

_____

_____

_____

_____

_____

_____

_____

_____

_____

_____

AP-3A LO 2 3 4

Kameria Inc. is a publicly traded company that manufactures high quality headsets. The company has asked you to recommend a method of inventory costing. The company will use your recommendation to create the company's quarterly income statements. The following data are for the first two quarters of 2019.

	Q1	Q2
Variable Manufacturing Costs per unit manufactured	$50	$50
Variable Advertising Costs per unit sold	$35	$35
Fixed Manufacturing Overhead Costs	$420,000	$420,000
Fixed Advertising Costs	$105,000	$105,000
Selling Price per unit	$125	$125
Beginning Inventory (units)	0	38,000
Production Volume	120,000	120,000
Sales Volume	82,000	155,000

The company's policies used to prepare internal reports for management are closely aligned with the policies used to prepare statements for external users.

Required

a) For each quarter, prepare a contribution margin statement under variable costing.

_____

_____

_____

Kameria Inc. Contribution Margin Statement For the First Two Quarters in 2019				
	Q1		Q2	

b) For each quarter, prepare an income statement under absorption costing.

_____
_____
_____
_____
_____
_____
_____
_____

Kameria Inc. Income Statement For the First Two Quarters in 2019				
	Q1		Q2	

Analysis

Which costing method would you recommend that the company use for internal decision-making, and why?

_____
_____
_____
_____
_____
_____
_____
_____
_____
_____
_____

AP-4A LO 3

During the most recent year Fixed Company (FC) reported the following income statement:

Sales	$240,000,000
Manufacturing Costs	165,000,000
Gross Margin	75,000,000
Selling, General and Administrative Costs	36,000,000
Income	$39,000,000

The FC financial officer has asked you to recast the income statement using the contribution margin (variable cost) approach. Units sold equals units produced.

Additional Information:

- FC produces a single product. It produced and sold 1,200,000 units of that product.
- For each unit sold the sales force is paid 10% of the product price minus its variable manufacturing cost.
- A student who recently spent a co-op term at FC did a regression analysis of manufacturing results for the past five years. The regression results suggest that the variable manufacturing cost per unit is $125. However, the co-op student also did a detailed study of the manufacturing process and that study suggested that the variable manufacturing cost per unit is $118.00.

Develop a contribution margin income statement for FC comparing two assumptions side by side. In one column, assume that the variable manufacturing cost per unit is $125. In the other column, assume that the variable manufacturing cost per unit is $118.

	VMC $125	VMC $118

Analysis

What is one advantage and one disadvantage of using each of the two variable manufacturing cost estimates?

_____

_____

_____

_____

_____

_____

_____

AP-5A LO 2 3

Pine Company reported the following Income statement under absorption costing for the year just ended.

Revenue	$15,000,000
Cost of Goods Sold	11,500,000
Gross Margin	3,500,000
Selling, General and Administrative Costs	3,000,000
Income	$500,000

You have asked supervisors to provide you with any additional information that they have. You received the following information in response.

- From the VP of Administration: Fixed selling and administrative cost per unit = $0.50
- From the VP of Manufacturing: Total Fixed Manufacturing = $2,500,000
- From the VP of Finance: Contribution Margin Ratio = 30.00%

Use the information above to recast this income statement to a contribution margin format income statement under variable costing.

Analysis

Use your answer above to develop an absorption format income statement for the upcoming year where sales are expected to be 3,200,000 units.

AP-6A LO 5

Mark It! Company developed a brand new product called the Mood Marker. The marker will release different colors in response to the user's emotional state. The markers currently cost the company $0.70 each and the company is planning to sell at 50% markup on cost. Determine the selling price, if the cost plus method is used.

AP-7A LO 5

Nicely Nails has been providing manicures in a local mall for several years. Recently, Nicely Nails has thought about expanding its business to include pedicures. Based on its analysis, it has learned that variable costs for pedicures include the cost of nail polish, remover, cotton balls and various lotions. The company's owners estimate that the variable cost per client will be about $5. To do pedicures, the company will need to buy specialized massage chairs with sinks built into them. Each one of these chairs can handle 12 customers per day and costs $100 per day to operate.

The owner of the company has provided you with the following data and has asked that you to analyze the information to let them know how much they should charge for the new service. Complete the table and then explain your answer.

Price per Unit	Quantity Demanded	Sales	Variable Costs	Contribution Margin	Fixed Costs	Income from Operations
$20.00	24					
25.00	20					
30.00	17					
35.00	15					
40.00	10					

AP-8A LO 5

Marksman DVD Company (Marksman) manufactures portable DVD players. The company requires a 20% rate of return on its investments. To start up the business, an investment of $500,000 was required. General and administrative expenses total $600,000. Each year, the sales volume is equal to 20,000 DVD players, each with a unit product cost of $110. Assuming that the company uses the formula method, determine the markup percentage that Marksman would apply in a cost plus pricing scheme.

AP-9A LO 5

Treason Solutions is considering using the target costing method to determine a selling price for one of its new products. An analysis of similar products on the market suggests a price of $150 each. If the company requires a profit of $95 per unit, what target cost should be set for the new product?

_____

_____

_____

_____

_____

_____

_____

_____

AP-10A LO 5

At the JIHL Company, a new auto part is being designed by the engineering team. Both the accounting and marketing department are asked to evaluate the product and use the target pricing method to determine the target cost of the new product. Currently, the company's competitors are selling a similar auto part for $130 per unit. JIHL Company requires a profit of 45% of the selling price.

_____

_____

_____

_____

_____

_____

_____

_____

_____

_____

_____

_____

_____

_____

_____

_____

_____

Application Questions Group B

AP-1B LO 2 3

Micro Company (MC) has reported the following information for the past two years.

	Year 1	Year 2	Year 3
Beginning Inventory	0	5,000	3,000
Production (units)	250,000	252,000	
Sales (units)	245,000	245,000	
Selling Price per Unit	$56.00	$59.00	
Variable Manufacturing Cost per Unit	$32.00	$31.00	
Variable Selling Cost per Unit	$5.60	$5.90	
Total Fixed Manufacturing Costs	$3,100,000	$2,900,000	
Non-Manufacturing Fixed Costs	$1,300,000	$1,350,000	

Required

a) Prepare income statements for Years 1 and 2 using the absorption costing approach assuming that MC uses first-in-first-out costing.

b) Prepare contribution margin income statements for years 1 and 2 using the variable costing approach.

Analysis

In this case, can income from operations under absorption costing be calculated based on the following information: income from operations under variable costing, fixed manufacturing overhead in inventory at the start of the year, and fixed manufacturing overhead in inventory at the end of the year? If so, what is the formula to calculate income from operations under absorption costing based on the given information?

_____

_____

_____

_____

_____

AP-2B LO 2 3 4

Nextar Company provides the following information for 2019:

	2019
Variable Manufacturing Costs per Unit Manufactured	$40
Variable Advertising Costs per Unit Sold	$25
Fixed Manufacturing Overhead Costs	$220,000
Fixed Advertising Costs	$130,000
Selling Price per Unit	$95
Beginning Inventory (Units)	0
Production Volume	20,000
Sales Volume	12,000

Required

a) Prepare a contribution margin statement for the year using the variable costing method.

_____

_____

_____

_____

_____

_____

_____

_____

_____

_____

_____

_____

Nextar Company Contribution Margin Statement For the Year Ending on December 31, 2019		

b) Prepare an income statement for the year using the absorption costing method.

_____

_____

_____

_____

_____

_____

Nextar Company Income Statement For the Year Ending on December 31, 2019		

c) Explain why there is a difference between the income from operations amounts under absorption costing and variable costing.

_____

_____

_____

_____

_____

_____

_____

AP-3B LO 3

Brass Values produces two types of valves used in production equipment. Brass Values reported the following income statement under absorption costing for the year ended December 31, 2019.

Brass Values Income Statement - Absorption Costing For the Year Ending December 31, 2019	
Sales Revenue	$1,625,000
Cost of Goods Sold	1,070,000
Gross Profit	555,000
Operating Expenses	495,000
Income from Operations	$60,000

The company president is very unhappy with the results and would like to have more information on the contribution provided by each of the two products to overall company profit. The controller has provided the following information:

	Valve 1	Valve 2
Unit Sales	25,000	50,000
Fixed Manufacturing Cost	$125,000	$145,000
Fixed Non-Manufacturing Cost	$85,000	$110,000
Contribution Margin Ratio	20%	40%
Revenue	$625,000	$1,000,000
% of Total Variable Manufacturing Cost	50%	50%

The number of units produced in 2019 is equal to the number of units sold. Use the information provided to produce a contribution margin income statement under variable costing to show the contribution of the two products to total income from operations.

Analysis

The president was thinking about an advertising campaign that is expected to change the sales of valves 1 and 2 to 35,000 and 45,000, respectively, as the company would pick up new customers but some current customers of valve 2 would switch their purchases to valve 1. What would be the effect of this promotion before considering the cost of the advertising campaign?

Per Unit	Valve 1	Valve 2	
	Valve 1	Valve 2	Total

AP-4B LO 3

The accountant at Long Gone Company (LGC) has disappeared and the company needs to prepare a contribution margin income statement for the year ending December 31, 2019. The following information has been found scattered on the missing accountant's desk:

1. The ratio of income to revenue: −10.75%
2. Income: −$322,500
3. Contribution margin ratio: 59.25%
4. Ratio of variable manufacturing costs to revenue: 40%
5. Other fixed costs are 75% of manufacturing fixed costs

Using this information construct LGC contribution margin income statement assuming that units produced equals units sold.

AP-5B LO 3

Status Company reported the following income statement under absorption costing for the year ending December 31, 2019.

Sales Revenue	$17,500,000
Cost of Goods Sold	10,200,000
Gross Profit	7,300,000
Operating Expenses	5,800,000
Income from Operations	$1,500,000

In addition, the financial records provided the following information:

- Contribution Margin Ratio = 32.00%
- Ratio of Variable Manufacturing Costs to Price per Unit = 44.00%
- Contribution Margin per Unit = $16.00

Use the information provided above to recast the contribution margin income statement under variable costing. Assume that the company produced and sold 350,000 units in 2019.

Analysis

Using the above contribution margin income statement in your answer above, and assuming all the relationships remain the same, estimate the income from operations for Status Company if sales are 375,000.

AP-6B LO 5

Florian is interested in starting up a business selling a special backpack for students. The bag has a variety of useful compartments for electronic devices, books and writing materials that are easy to access and stylish. After doing some market research, Florian has discovered the following data:

Expected Sales (units)	Selling Price
1,850	$50.00
1,200	75.00
1,000	85.00
600	100.00
350	120.00

Additional Information:

- Each bag requires $8.50 of direct materials, $14.75 in direct labor, variable manufacturing overhead of $1.25 and variable selling costs of $1.75.
- Fixed costs are $10.00 per unit based on 1,000 units of production.

Assuming Florian uses absorption costing, what should Florian sell the bags for? Why should he not just sell them for $120?

Selling Price	Expected Sales (units)	Sales	Variable Costs	Contribution Margin	Fixed Costs	Income from Operations

_____

_____

_____

_____

AP-7B LO 5

Alexon Limited is considering producing a new line of high quality snowboards. The company will incur $60 in variable product costs for each snowboard produced. Fixed manufacturing overhead costs amount to $165,000.

Required

a) Assume that the company has a policy to set product prices equal to the variable cost plus 80%. Determine how much the company would sell each snowboard for.

_____

_____

_____

_____

_____

_____

b) Assume that the company has a pricing policy that requires its products to be sold at full cost plus 60%. For the upcoming year, it believes it can produce and sell a total of 6,000 snowboards. Determine how much the company would sell each snowboard for.

_____

_____

_____

_____

_____

_____

_____

AP-8B `LO` `1` `5`

Sancon Manufacturing provides the following budget for next year:

	Budgeted Costs
Direct Materials	$12 per gram
Direct Labor	$20 per direct labor hour
Variable Manufacturing Overhead	$5 per direct labor hour
Fixed Manufacturing Overhead	$930,000
General and Administrative Expenses	$1,550,000

Sancon Manufacturing only produces one product. Assume variable product costs are the only variable costs incurred by the company. Each unit requires 40 grams of direct materials and five direct labor hours. In the market, competitors are selling a similar product for $750 each. The company estimates it will produce and sell 30,000 units next year regardless of the price it sets for the product. Normally, the company desires an income from operations of $2,900,000.

Required

a) The company has a pricing policy of selling its product at a price equal to variable product cost plus a markup of 30%.

      i. What is the selling price for the product?

     ii. What is the estimated contribution margin?

   iii. Based on current budgeted sales and costs, will the company meet its desired level of income from operations?

b) Now assume that the company has a cost plus pricing policy and uses absorption (full) cost as the cost base. The markup percentage is equal to 20%.

    i. What is the selling price for the product?

    ii. What is the estimated contribution margin?

    iii. Based on current budgeted sales and costs, will the company meet its desired level of income from operations?

_____

_____

_____

_____

_____

_____

_____

_____

_____

_____

_____

_____

_____

_____

c) The company has assumed that it will produce and sell a certain number of units next year regardless of the price it sets for the product. Is this a reasonable assumption?

_____

_____

_____

AP-9B LO 1 5

Lodrobe Company manufactures a single product: wardrobes. Lodrobe's wardrobes have a unique design that is not replicated by any other wardrobe manufacturer. The company was formed at the beginning of last year with an initial investment of $800,000. Lodrobe requires a 25% annual rate of return on the investment. In total, 10,000 wardrobes were produced and sold last year. For the upcoming year, the production and sales volumes are not expected to change from last year. The following costs are budgeted for the upcoming year:

	Per Unit	Total (10,000 units)
Direct materials	$80	
Direct labor	$70	
Variable manufacturing overhead	$25	
Fixed manufacturing overhead	-	$100,000
General and administrative expenses	-	$400,000

To price its product, Lodrobe uses the cost plus pricing method. The company has a policy of using the absorption costing method for assigning costs to inventory and the formula method for determining a markup percentage.

Required

a) Determine the budgeted full cost per unit (a wardrobe) for the upcoming year.

_____

_____

_____

b) Calculate the markup percentage.

_____

_____

_____

_____

_____

c) Prepare a price quote sheet to determine the selling price of a wardrobe for the upcoming year.

_____

_____

_____

_____

_____

_____

_____

_____

_____

AP-10B LO 5

Kawson Company has recently developed a new product. The product will be sold in the market next month. Based on market research, similar products are sold at $350 per unit. The company requires a profit of 35% of selling price. Assume the company uses the target pricing method.

a) What is the target cost per unit?

_____

_____

_____

_____

_____

b)   The company realized that the product cannot be produced to meet the target cost. What is another option the company has for choosing a selling price? Explain.

Critical Thinking

CT-1

Jason Craven (JC) Incorporated is a public company that produces and distributes high quality surround sound speakers. The company's suppliers provide a deep discount if it makes large purchases. As a result, JC's production volume is often greater than its sales volume for a given period. In 2019, the company produced 120,000 speakers, but sold only 55,000 speakers. The company provides the following cost information:

Variable Cost per Unit	
Direct Materials	$12
Direct Labor	$20
Variable Manufacturing Overhead Costs	$8
Variable General and Administrative Costs per unit sold	$5
Annual Fixed Costs	
Fixed Manufacturing Overhead Costs	$600,000
Fixed General and Administrative Costs	$35,000

The company uses the cost plus pricing system to determine the appropriate selling price for its speakers. If the company decides to use the absorption cost as the base, the markup percentage would be 25%. If the company decides to use the variable manufacturing cost as the base, the markup percentage would be 35%.

Required

a) Calculate the selling price for each of the two pricing strategies (i.e. using the variable manufacturing cost or the absorption cost as the base).

b) For each of the selling prices calculated in part a), create an income statement to determine income from operations. Which selling price will generate the highest income from operations?

Jason Craven Incorporated Income Statement For the Year Ending December 31, 2019		

Jason Craven Incorporated Income Statement For the Year Ending December 31, 2019		

_____

_____

_____

_____

_____

_____

_____

_____

_____

_____

c) The company's sales manager estimates that the speakers cannot be priced more than $60. At this price, management thinks that they can sell 50,000 speakers. The initial investment in producing the speakers is $1,500,000 and the company's desires a 20% on return on investment. Using the target costing method, should the company set the price per speaker at $60?

Case Study

CS-1 LO 1

Harson Company manufactures and sells tables. The company provides the following data for the product:

Selling Price per Unit	$42
Variable Cost per Unit:	
Variable Manufacturing Costs	$12
Variable General and Administrative Costs per unit sold	$14
Annual Fixed Costs:	
Fixed Manufacturing Overhead Costs	$600,000
Fixed General and Administrative Costs	$350,000

The company produced 120,000 units and sold 55,000 units this year.

The accounting department has prepared the following absorption costing income statement for 2019:

Harson Company Income Statement For the Year Ending on December 31, 2019		
Revenues		$2,310,000
Cost of Goods Sold		
Beginning Inventory	$0	
Variable Manufacturing Costs	1,440,000	
Fixed Manufacturing Overhead Costs	600,000	
Cost of Goods Available for Sale	2,040,000	
Ending Inventory	1,105,000	935,000
Gross Margin		1,375,000
Operating Expenses		
General and Administrative Costs		1,120,000
Income from Operations		$255,000

Required

a) How many units would the company need to sell in order to break even? Use the formula introduced in chapter 5.

_____

_____

_____

_____

_____

b) Assume that the amount of units sold is less than the breakeven point calculated in part a). Explain to the CEO why the company can still generate a positive income from operations even though the annual sales volume is less than the breakeven point.

_____

_____

_____

_____

_____

_____

_____

_____

_____

_____

_____

_____

_____

_____

_____

_____

_____

_____

_____

_____

_____

_____

_____

_____

_____

_____

_____

_____

_____

_____

_____

_____

_____

_____

_____

_____

Chapter 7

MASTER BUDGET

LEARNING OBJECTIVES

LO 1 Identify the benefits of budgeting

LO 2 Describe different approaches to budgeting

LO 3 Describe the components and information flows of the master budgeting process

LO 4 Prepare operating budgets

LO 5 Prepare a capital budget

LO 6 Prepare a cash budget

LO 7 Prepare a budgeted balance sheet

LO 8 Apply budgeting to a service company or merchandising company

LO 9 Describe ethical considerations to budgeting

AMEENGAGE *Access **ameengage.com** for integrated resources including tutorials, practice exercises, the digital textbook and more.*

Assessment Questions

AS-1 LO 1

What is a budget?

AS-2 LO 1

What are two benefits of budgeting?

AS-3 LO 3

What does a master budget represent?

AS-4 LO 4

List the different budgets contained in the operating budget of a manufacturing firm.

_____

_____

AS-5 LO 4

What is the first step of creating an operating budget?

_____

_____

AS-6 LO 4

What does the production budget forecast?

_____

_____

_____

AS-7 LO 5

What information is contained in the capital budget?

_____

_____

_____

AS-8 LO 6

Why is it important to prepare a cash budget?

_____

_____

_____

_____

AS-9 LO 1

How are budgets used for planning and controlling?

_____

_____

_____

_____

_____

_____

AS-10 LO 2

Describe zero-based budgets and incremental budgets and identify the difference between the two.

_____

_____

_____

_____

AS-11 LO 2

Provide one advantage and one disadvantage of using zero-based budgeting.

_____

_____

_____

_____

AS-12 LO 2

Provide one advantage and one disadvantage of using incremental budgeting.

_____

_____

_____

_____

AS-13 LO 2

What is the difference between top-down and bottom-up budgeting?

_____

_____

_____

_____

AS-14 LO 2

What is budgetary slack and what is its impact on an organization?

_____

_____

_____

AS-15 LO 8

Provide an example of how budgeting in a merchandising company is different from budgeting in a manufacturing company.

_____

_____

AS-16 LO 9

What are some characteristics of ethically set goals?

_____

_____

_____

--- **Application Questions Group A** ---

AP-1A LO 4

For the upcoming year, Leche Gallon Limited expects to generate $3,900,000 of revenue. Based on historical trends, the company makes the most sales in the fourth quarter. As a result, it assumes that the fourth quarter will contribute 60% of the annual revenue. The remaining budgeted amount will be allocated equally between the other three quarters.

For each quarter, calculate the budgeted sales in dollars.

Q1	Q2	Q3	Q4	Period End

AP-2A LO 4

ACME Company manufactures televisions. The company estimated there will be 47,700 units in inventory at the beginning of December 2019. ACME wants to have half of that amount in its inventory at the end of December. Based on the forecasted sales, 118,900 televisions will be sold in the month of December.

Required

a) Determine the number of televisions to be produced in December.

_____

_____

_____

b) Prepare a production budget.

ACME Company Production Budget Month Ending December 31, 2019	

AP-3A LO 4

The ThirstBuster Company is famous for its energy drinks. The company expects to produce 2,153,000 bottles of energy drink in 2019. ThirstBuster purchases empty bottles from Bottle Bro Inc. In 2018, ThirstBuster had 24,100 empty bottles in ending inventory. For 2019, ThirstBuster has planned to have 75,700 empty bottles in ending inventory.

Calculate the number of empty bottles that ThirstBuster should purchase from Bottle Bro Inc. in 2019.

AP-4A LO 4

The Shoe For You Company manufactures two types of shoes; dress and casual shoes. For the month of May, the company plans to produce 21,000 pairs of dress shoes and 17,500 pairs of casual shoes. Both types of shoes are produced in the assembling and finishing departments. The direct labor rates for assembling and finishing departments are $13.00 per hour and $17.50 per hour, respectively. The following table indicates the amount of direct labor hours required for each type of shoe:

	Assembling	Finishing
Dress shoes	15 minutes per pair	30 minutes per pair
Casual shoes	10 minutes per pair	15 minutes per pair

Calculate the budgeted direct labor cost.

	Production Units	**Assembling**				**Finishing**		
		Cost per unit of input ($/hour)	Amount of Inputs per unit (minutes)	Total		Cost per unit of input ($/hour)	Amount of Inputs per unit (minutes)	Total

_____

_____

_____

_____

_____

AP-5A LO 4

Rosen Inc. manufactures skateboards. The company estimated September 2019's direct labor amount to be 25,000 hours. The company allocates its manufacturing overhead based on direct labor hours. Last year, the company budgeted 20,000 direct labor hours and manufacturing overhead costs amount to $15,000.

Required

a) Calculate the predetermined overhead rate using last year's budget.

_____

_____

_____

b) Using the predetermined overhead rate in part a), determine the manufacturing overhead budget for September 2019.

_____

_____

_____

AP-6A LO 7

Joe Barker is the production manager of Auto Parts Company (APC) and has been asked to prepare 2020's ending finished goods budget for the S222 product. Based on historical figures, Joe determines the following information regarding direct materials, direct labor and manufacturing overhead for the S222 product.

Direct Materials Costs per Unit	$1.10 per unit
Direct Labor Cost per Direct Labor Hour (DLH)	$15 per DLH
DLH per Unit	0.25 DLH per unit
Predetermined Manufacturing Overhead Rate	$4 per DLH

Assume APC targets 5,000 units of S222 for ending inventory at the end of 2020. Calculate the value of S222 inventory that will be recorded in 2020's budgeted balance sheet.

AP-7A LO 5

Jolly Jalapenos Inc. has decided to purchase new capital equipment costing $500,000 cash in the next fiscal year. It also intends to sell its old equipment for $35,000 cash.

Prepare the capital budget for Jolly Jalapenos Inc. for its upcoming year end (December 31, 2019).

AP-8A LO 6

Super Computers expects $750,000 of total sales in February and $690,000 of total sales in March. Historically, the company collects 59% of its total sales in the month of sale and 41% in the following month.

Determine the amount of cash that the company expects to collect in the month of March.

AP-9A LO 6

Ariel Johns provides the following budgets for cash receipts and cash disbursements for 2019 on a quarterly basis. The ending cash balance on December 31, 2018 was $18,500.

	Q1	Q2	Q3	Q4	Period End
Receipts	$39,000	$28,000	$12,000	$48,000	$127,000
Disbursements	$20,000	$33,000	$18,000	$33,000	$104,000

Required

a) Calculate the net cash flow for each quarter.

	Q1	Q2	Q3	Q4
Net Cash Flow				

b) Calculate the ending cash balance for each quarter.

	Q1	Q2	Q3	Q4
Opening Balance				
Net Cash Flow				
Ending Balance				

AP-10A `LO 6`

Joseph Lawrence will be opening his company called JL Company in January of next year. He predicts that January, February and March will generate $150,000, $120,000 and $135,000 worth of sales, respectively. The company expects to sell 30% of its products for cash. Sixty percent of the sales on account are expected to be collected in the month of the sale, 30% in the month following the sale and the remainder in the following month. Prepare the cash receipts section of the cash budget.

JL Company Cash Receipts For January, February and March			

AP-11A `LO 4 6`

Buildup Sports Inc. is a retailer of shoes and sports gear. The following is Buildup Sports' sales forecast by quarter for the upcoming year.

Buildup Sports Inc. Forecasted Sales For the Year Ended December 31, 2020					
	Q1	Q2	Q3	Q4	Period End
Sales	$107,000	$289,000	$361,000	$236,000	$993,000

In addition, sales in Q3 and Q4 of 2019 totaled $128,000 and $209,000, respectively. According to the company's sales records, 63% of sales are made in cash and the remaining 37% are made on account (i.e. credit sales). Assume the following historical trends were noted by management regarding credit sales:

47% of credit customers pay during the quarter in which the sale took place
28% of credit customers pay in the quarter immediately following the quarter of sale
20% of credit customers pay in the second quarter following the quarter of sale
The remaining 5% of credit sales are uncollectible

Required

a)   Calculate the forecasted sales for each quarter (separate revenue into cash and credit sales).

	Q1	Q2	Q3	Q4	Period End
Buildup Sports Inc.					

Table title: Buildup Sports Inc. / Forecasted Sales / For the Year Ended December 31, 2020

b)   Prepare the cash receipts section of the 2020 cash budget (on a quarterly basis)

Receipts:	Q1	Q2	Q3	Q4	Period End

Table title: Buildup Sports Inc. / Cash Receipts / For the Year Ended December 31, 2020

AP-12A `LO 4 6`

Sharp Inc. is a manufacturer of curling irons. Each curling iron sells for $28. The budgeted sales in units for the upcoming months in 2019 are as follows:

Month	Units
April	5,100
May	5,680
June	5,570
July	5,350

Sharp Inc.'s collection pattern for sales are as follows: 15% of sales are cash, the remaining 85% are on credit. For credit sales 50% is collected in the month of sale, 45% is collected in the month following the sale and 5% is uncollectible. As at March 31, 2019 there was a total of $35,000 in accounts receivable to be collected in April.

a)   Prepare a sales budget for the second quarter.

	April	May	June	Period End

Table title: Sharp Inc. / Sales Budget / Q2 Ended, June 30, 2019

b) Prepare a schedule of cash receipts for the second quarter.

Sharp Inc. Schedule of Cash Receipts Q2 Ended, June 30, 2019				
	April	**May**	**June**	**Period End**

AP-13A LO 6

Hype Sports Inc. is a retailer of clothing and sports equipment. Management has collected the following information regarding budgeted disbursements for the upcoming year.

Operating expenses are expected to be evenly distributed through the year at $138,800 each quarter. New capital is expected to be purchased for $506,000 in the first quarter. Half will be paid for in the second quarter and half will be paid for in the third quarter.

Dividends of $40,300 will be paid in the fourth quarter.

Prepare the cash disbursements section of the 2019 cash budget (on a quarterly basis)

Hype Sports Inc. Cash Disbursements For the Year Ended December 31, 2019					
	Q1	**Q2**	**Q3**	**Q4**	**Period End**

AP-14A LO **7**

Norah, the sole stockholder of Marshall Inc., runs a home-cleaning service in the suburb of a large city. Her balance sheet as at May 31, 2019 is as follows:

Marshall Inc. Balance Sheet As at May 31, 2019	
Assets	
Cash	$5,000
Accounts Receivable	15,000
Equipment	9,000
Accumulated Depreciation	(1,000)
Total Assets	$28,000
Liabilities	
Accounts Payable	3,000
Notes Payable	13,000
Total Liabilities	16,000
Stockholders' Equity	12,000
Total Liabilities and Stockholder's Equity	$28,000

In the upcoming year, Norah expects the following events to occur:

- Total revenues of $25,000 and total expenses of $10,000
- 100% of accounts receivable from the prior year will be collected in the following year
- Credit sales will represent 50% of revenues for the year
- 100% of accounts payable owing from 2019 will be paid off in 2020
- By the end of May, 2020, Marshall will owe its suppliers $3,500
- No principal payments will be made on the note payable during 2020
- Purchase of new equipment for $2,000. The entire purchase will be financed through a note payable
- Expect to have a cash balance of $23,800 at the end of fiscal 2020
- Depreciate assets by $800 during 2020

Prepare Marshall Inc.'s budgeted balance sheet as at May 31, 2020.

Marshall Inc. Budgeted Balance Sheet As at May 31, 2020	

AP-15A LO 4 6

a) Sodor Inc. is a manufacturer of toy trains. Each train sells for $15. Sodor's estimated sales for the first five months of the 2019 fiscal year are as follows:

Month	Sales in Units
January	15,000
February	18,000
March	21,000
April	27,000
May	25,000

Prepare the **sales budget** for the first quarter.

Sodor Inc. Sales Budget For the Quarter Ended March 31, 2019				
	January	February	March	Period End

b) When compiling the annual budget, the production manager insists that extra inventory should be on hand in case actual sales are higher than budgeted. The production manager has determined that 15% of the following month's budgeted sales should be sufficient for the extra inventory. Ending inventory at December 31, 2018 was 3,000 units.

Prepare the **production budget** for the first quarter.

Sodor Inc. Production Budget For the Quarter Ended March 31, 2019				
	January	**February**	**March**	**Period End**

c) Each toy train requires 3 pounds (lbs) of materials and each pound costs $0.50. Management budgets for extra materials in the event that there is a shortage from suppliers. Management would like to have 20% of the following month's production needs in ending inventory each month. Ending inventory of train materials at December 31, 2018 is 9,500 lbs.

Prepare the direct materials budget and purchasing budget for the first quarter.

Sodor Inc. Direct Material Purchases Budget For the Quarter Ended March 31, 2019				
	January	**February**	**March**	**Period End**

Sodor Inc. Purchasing Budget For the Quarter Ended March 31, 2019				
	January	**February**	**March**	**Period End**

d) Sodor's sales history indicates that 35% of sales will be for cash and 65% of sales will be on credit. Using the information from the sales budget, the forecasted cash and credit sales can be determined:

Sodor Inc. Forecasted Cash Sales and Credit Sales For the Quarter Ended March 31, 2019	January	February	March	Period End

Sodor has reviewed past collection history and has determined that credit sales will be collected as follows: 70% is collected in the month of sale and 30% is collected the following month. The total credit sales for the month of December 31, 2018 were $125,000.

Prepare the budgeted schedule of cash receipts for the first quarter.

Sodor Inc. Schedule of Cash Receipts For the Quarter Ended March 31, 2019	January	February	March	Period End

e) Sodor will pay for 60% of its purchases of material in the month the material is purchased, and the remaining 40% in the following month. The total credit purchases for the month of December 31, 2018 were $35,000.

Prepare the budgeted schedule of cash disbursements for the first quarter.

Sodor Inc. Schedule of Cash Disbursements For the Quarter Ended March 31, 2019	January	February	March	Period End

f) Prepare a cash budget for the first quarter.

Assume the following:

1) Sodor started the year with $20,000 in its bank account and must maintain a minimum cash balance of $10,000 at the end of each month.

2) Sodor has access to an open line of credit with the bank to borrow money if needed. To keep things simple, ignore interest calculations on the bank borrowings. Also, loan borrowings are taken in multiples of $1,000.

3) Sodor maintains that they will repay debts as soon as possible with any excess cash that becomes available.

4) Sodor has budgeted the following for 2019:
   - Payment for operating expenses = $105,000 each month.
   - Depreciation expense is $5,400 a month.
   - Sodor will need to purchase new machinery. The total cost of the machinery is $180,000. Sodor will pay $100,000 in January and $80,000 in February.
   - Cash dividends of $75,000 will be paid to shareholders in February and March.

Sodor Inc. Cash Budget For the Quarter Ended March 31, 2019				
	January	February	March	Period End

AP-16A LO 6

Advantage Corp. requires a minimum cash balance of $100 at the end of each quarter. Complete the cash budget for Advantage Corp by filling in the grey areas below.

Advantage Corp. Cash Budget For the Year Ended December 31, 2019	Q1	Q2	Q3	Q4	Period End
Cash (Beginning)	$165				
Cash Receipts:					
Cash from Sales		425			1,915
Collections from Credit Customers	630		465		2,315
Total Cash Available	1,235	1,345		1,455	4,395
Cash Disbursements:					
Manufacturing Costs	290	340		225	1,115
General and Admin. costs		640	335		1,600
Capital Expenditures	350	525	280		1,505
Dividend Payment		15	135		
Total Cash Disbursements		1,520	1,010		4,370
Cash Excess (Deficit)	345		(105)		
Financing Requirements:					
Loan Borrowings					
Loan Repayments					
Ending Cash Balance _____					

AP-17A LO 4

SJP Corp. designs and manufactures handbags and their products are distributed to department stores. SJP has budgeted the following sales in units for the upcoming year:

Quarter	Units
Q1 - 2019	2,600
Q2 - 2019	2,350
Q3 - 2019	2,800
Q4 - 2019	2,550
Q1 - 2020	2,400
Q2 - 2020	2,750

In preparing the annual budgets, management believes that an extra 8% of the following quarter's budgeted sales units is necessary to prevent a shortage of inventory. Inventory on hand as at December 31, 2018 was 160 units.

Each handbag requires 2 yards of leather. As at December 31, 2018 there were 850 yards of leather on hand in the warehouse. To prepare against a shortage of supplies, management budgets to have 25% of the following quarter's budgeted leather needs in ending inventory each quarter. Each yard of leather costs $25.

Required

a)   Prepare a production budget by quarter and for the year in total.

SJP Corp. Production Budget (# Units) For the Year Ended December 31, 2019					
	Q1	**Q2**	**Q3**	**Q4**	**Period End**

b)   Prepare a direct materials budget.

SJP Corp. DM Purchases Budget For the Year Ended December 31, 2019					
	Q1	**Q2**	**Q3**	**Q4**	**Period End**

AP-18A LO 4 6

Braun Inc. manufactures scooters. Each scooter requires 2 tires. To prepare against a shortage in supplies, when budgeting for the number of tires needed, management likes to have an extra 15% of each month's budgeted needs. Each tire costs $50 to purchase. As at December 31, 2018, there were a total of 1,000 tires in the warehouse.

Braun purchases tires from a supplier who allows Braun to pay for 65% of its purchases in the month of purchase and the remaining 35% in the following month. For the month of December 2018, Braun had a total of $480,000 in purchases from the supplier.

a) Complete the direct materials budget for Braun Inc.

Braun Inc. DM Purchases Budget Q1 Ended, March 31, 2019				
	January	February	March	Period End
Budgeted Production (# units)	4,800	5,150	5,000	14,950

b) Prepare a schedule of cash disbursements for Braun Inc.

Braun Inc. Schedule of Cash Disbursements Q1 Ended, March 31, 2019				
	January	February	March	Period End

AP-19A LO 6

Hudson Inc. is a manufacturer of patio furniture. Management has asked that a cash budget be prepared for the upcoming year. The following is the company's budgeted information for the 2019 fiscal year:

	Q1	Q2	Q3	Q4	Period End
Sales (all on credit)	32,000	25,700	34,500	41,800	134,000
Direct Material Purchases	14,400	11,565	15,525	14,630	56,120
Direct Labor	12,800	10,280	13,800	12,540	49,420
Rent expense	2,600	2,600	2,600	2,600	16,080
Depreciation expense	3,200	2,570	3,450	4,180	13,400

Additional information is as follows:

- Hudson requires ending cash balance for each period to be at a minimum of $5,000. The ending cash balance at Q4-2018 was $5,350.
- All sales are on credit. The collection pattern for sales is 80% in the quarter of sale, 20% in the following quarter.
- There were no outstanding accounts receivable as at Q4-2018.
- Direct materials are paid for in full in the quarter following the purchase.
- The total purchases in Q4-2018 were $9,200.
- All other expenses will be paid in full in the quarter they are budgeted for.

- Equipment costing a total of $15,000 is to be purchased in the year; $8,000 will be paid in Q2 and $7,000 in Q3.
- Dividend payments of $3,000 is to be paid in Q3 and $3,500 in Q4.
- Hudson has an open line of credit which is used for any borrowings the company may need. Any borrowings are done in multiples of $1,000.

a) Complete a schedule of cash receipts for the 2019 fiscal year.

	Q1	Q2	Q3	Q4	Period End
Hudson Inc. **Schedule of Cash Receipts** **For the Year Ended December 31, 2019**					

b) Prepare a cash budget for the 2019 fiscal year.

	Q1	Q2	Q3	Q4	Period End
Hudson Inc. **Cash Budget** **For the Year Ended December 31, 2019**					

Application Questions Group B

AP-1B `LO 4`

For the upcoming year, Kinston Quart Limited expects to generate $4,000,000 of revenue. Based on historical trends, the company makes the most sales in the first two quarters. As a result, it assumes that the first and second quarter will each contribute 30% of the annual revenue. The remaining budgeted amount will be allocated equally between the last two quarters.

Calculate budgeted sales in dollars for each quarter and the upcoming year as a whole.

Q1	Q2	Q3	Q4	Period End

AP-2B `LO 4`

BTL Company manufactures speaker systems. The company estimated there will be 50,000 units in inventory at the beginning of December 2019. BTL wants to have half of that amount in its inventory at the end of December. Based on the forecasted sales, 125,000 speaker systems will be sold in December.

Required

a) Determine the number of speakers to be produced in December.

_____

_____

_____

_____

b) Prepare a production budget.

BTL Company Production Budget For the Month Ending on December 31, 2019	

AP-3B `LO 4`

The KoolaKoola Company is famous for its pop drinks. The company expects to produce 2 million cans of soda in 2019. KoolaKoola purchases empty cans from Can Man Inc. In 2018, KoolaKoola had 24,000 empty cans in ending inventory. For 2019, KoolaKoola has planned to have 70,000 empty cans in ending inventory.

Calculate the number of empty cans that KoolaKoola should purchase from Can Man Inc. in 2019.

_____

_____

_____

_____

_____

_____

AP-4B LO 4

The following is Alpha Hardware Corporation's income statement for the year ended December 31, 2019:

Alpha Hardware Corporation **Income Statement** **For the Year Ending December 31, 2019**	
Revenues	$800,000
Cost of Goods Sold	480,000
Gross Profit	320,000
Expenses:	
Administrative Costs	25,000
Selling Costs	18,000
Salaries	95,000*
Rent	25,000
Total Expenses	163,000
Net Income	$157,000

*Comprised of $65,000 in managers' salaries and $30,000 in office employees' salaries

Alpha Hardware is a small business and it does not intend to spend a lot of time and money on budgeting. The manager has determined the 2020 budgeted income statement should simply reflect the following predicted changes from the 2019 income statement:

- Revenues will increase by 2.5%
- Gross profit will increase by 5%
- Selling costs will decrease by 3%
- Managers' salaries will increase by 8%
- Administrative costs, office employees' salaries, and rent expense will remain the same

Prepare the budgeted income statement for the year ending December 31, 2020 using the incremental budgeting approach.

Alpha Hardware Corporation Budgeted Income Statement For the Year Ending December 31, 2020	

AP-5B LO 4

Sammy Chum, the owner of SC Limited, prepared the following 2019 direct labor budget:

SC Limited Direct Labor Budget For the Year Ending December 31, 2019				
	Q1	**Q2**	**Q3**	**Q4**
Budgeted Direct Labor Hours	34,000	28,000	47,000	51,000
Direct Labor Cost per DLH	$15.00	$15.00	$15.00	$15.00
Budgeted Direct Labor Costs	$510,000	$420,000	$705,000	$765,000

For 2019, Sammy budgets $400,000 of manufacturing overhead. The budgeted manufacturing overhead cost is normally allocated based on the budgeted direct labor hours.

Determine the amount of budgeted manufacturing overhead for each quarter.

	Q1	**Q2**	**Q3**	**Q4**	**Period End**

AP-6B LO 6

Amanda Henderson is getting ready for her first year in university. In order to get funding from her parents, she is required to prepare a cash budget for the first semester.

Expected Expenditures:	
Tuition fees due on September 20	$2,500
Rent due at the beginning of each month	500
Food per month	265
Entertainment per month	110
Expected Income:	
Part-time job: Monthly wage	$370

For each month of the first semester (i.e. September, October, November and December), determine the amount of money that Amanda's parents should give her. Classes and rent start on September 1st. Assume that Amanda spends the same amount of money on food and entertainment every month.

_____

_____

_____

_____

_____

_____

_____

_____

_____

_____

_____

_____

_____

_____

_____

AP-7B LO 5

Bob's Bicycles Manufacturing Inc. (BBM), manufactures affordable bicycles for major metropolitan centers. BBM has a year end of July 31. On July 31, 2019, BBM had a $4,000 cash balance on its financial statements. Before the 2019 year end, BBM budgeted an amount of $230,000 cash for purchase of manufacturing equipment in 2020. It also planned to sell old equipment for a budgeted amount of $18,000 cash in 2020.

Prepare the capital budget for BBM for its upcoming year end (July 31, 2020).

AP-8B LO 6

Easy Computers expects $800,000 of total sales in January and $700,000 of total sales in February. Historically, the company collects 65% of its total sales in the month of sale and 35% in the following month.

Determine the amount of cash that the company expects to collect in the month of February.

_____

_____

_____

_____

AP-9B LO 6

Henry Lawrence provides the following budgets for cash receipts and cash disbursements for 2019 on a quarterly basis. The ending cash balance on December 31, 2018 was $18,500.

	Q1	Q2	Q3	Q4	Period End
Receipts	$34,000	$26,000	$14,000	$54,000	$128,000
Disbursements	20,000	30,000	15,000	30,000	95,000

Required

a) Calculate the net cash flow for each quarter.

	Q1	Q2	Q3	Q4

b) Calculate the ending cash balance for each quarter.

	Q1	Q2	Q3	Q4

AP-10B LO 6

Akma Inc. provides you with the following budgeted information:

	May	June	July
Sales	$510,000	$450,000	$550,000
Manufacturing Costs	150,000	280,000	250,000
Capital expenditures (machinery and buildings)	400,000	-	120,000
General and administration costs (excluding depreciation)	70,000	210,000	100,000

Expectations:

- Cash sales represent 10% of total sales.
- 70% of the credit sales is collected in the month of sale and the remaining 30% will be collected in the following month.
- The credit sales of April amounted to $400,000.
- 60% of any month's capital expenditures is to be paid at the end of the month. The remainder is to be paid in the following month.
- Manufacturing and general and administration costs are to be paid in the month in which they are incurred.
- Dividends of $3,000 are expected to be declared in June and paid in July.
- Akma Inc. must have at least a $10,000 cash balance at the end of each month.
- Excess cash over the required minimum cash balance has to be used towards paying off any outstanding notes payable. Ignore interests on notes payable.
- The balance of the note payable as of May 1 is $0.
- The balance of cash as of May 1 is $15,000.

Prepare a cash budget for each month in the quarter and the quarter as a whole.

Akma Inc. Cash Budget for May, June and July				
	May	**June**	**July**	**Period End**

_____

_____

_____

_____

_____

AP-11B LO 4 6

Holiday Inc. sells beach umbrellas for $15 each. The company's year end is December 31. The budgeted sales in units for 2019 are as follows:

Month	Units
July	10,800
August	16,800
September	14,400
October	12,000

Holiday's sales are all on account, (i.e. credit sales). Its collection pattern for credit sales is 65% is collected in the month of sale, 30% is collected in the month following the sale, and 5% is considered bad debts. The June 2019 total credit sales were $165,000.

a) Prepare a sales budget for Holiday Inc.

Holiday Inc. Sales Budget Q3 Ended, September 30, 2019				
	July	August	September	Period End

b) Prepare a schedule of cash receipts for Holiday Inc.

Holiday Inc. Schedule of Cash Receipts Q3 Ended, September 30, 2019				
	July	August	September	Period End

AP-12B LO 4 6

Hype Sports Inc. is a retailer of clothing and sports equipment. The following is Hype Sports' sales forecast by quarter for the upcoming year.

Hype Sports Inc. Forecasted Sales For the Year Ending December 31, 2019					
	Q1	**Q2**	**Q3**	**Q4**	**Period End**
Sales	$115,000	$300,000	$350,000	$250,000	$1,015,000

In addition, sales in Q3 and Q4 of 2018 totaled $135,000 and $200,000, respectively. According to the company's sales records, 60% of sales are made in cash and the remaining 40% are made on account (i.e. credit sales). Assume the following historical trends were noted by management regarding credit sales:

- 50% of credit customers pay during the quarter in which the sale took place
- 30% of credit customers pay in the quarter immediately following the quarter of sale
- 15% of credit customers pay in the second quarter following the quarter of sale
- The remaining 5% of credit sales are uncollectible

Required

a) Calculate the forecasted sales for each quarter (separate revenue into cash and credit sales).

Hype Sports Inc. Forecasted Sales For the Year Ending December 31, 2019					
	Q1	**Q2**	**Q3**	**Q4**	**Period End**

b) Prepare the cash receipts section of the 2019 cash budget (on a quarterly basis).

Hype Sports Inc. Cash Receipts For the Year Ending December 31, 2019					
	Q1	**Q2**	**Q3**	**Q4**	**Period End**

AP-13B LO 6

Tyler Sheen is the owner of MTE Incorporated. He provided the selected opening balances as at June 1, 2019 and the budgeted information for June and July 2019.

Selected Opening Balances as of June 1, 2019	
Cash	$75,000
Accounts Receivable	130,000
Inventory	240,000
Noncurrent Assets	100,000
Accounts Payable	50,000
Stockholder's Equity	640,000
Budgeted Amounts	
For the month of June:	
Total Revenue	$310,000
Total General and Administration Costs	195,000
Total Capital Expenditures	150,000
For the month of July:	
Total Revenue	410,000
Total General and Administration Costs	200,000
Total Capital Expenditures	250,000

The company's monthly depreciation represents 20% of general and administration costs. Sixty percent of the general and administration costs (excluding depreciation) are paid in the month in which they are incurred, and the rest is recorded in accounts payable to be paid in the next month. Of the $150,000 capital expenditures for June, $125,000 will be paid in July. The remaining amount will be paid in the month in which they are incurred.

Required

a) Calculate the total cash disbursement for the month of June.

_____

_____

_____

_____

_____

_____

_____

b) Calculate the total cash disbursement for the month of July.

_____

_____

_____

_____

_____
_____
_____
_____
_____

AP-14B [LO 7]

Charles Cocoa Corporation (CCC) has gathered the following data pertaining to the preparation of its 2020 budgeted balance sheet:

- Accounts receivable is typically 3% of sales revenue.
- The company has always maintained a cash balance of $57,000.
- CCC has budgeted $125,000 to purchase new machinery for 2020. CCC does not expect to sell any existing machinery. The purchase of machinery will be financed entirely through a note payable.
- Depreciation expense for 2020 is expected to amount to $5,000.
- Total budgeted revenue is $200,000 and total budgeted expenses is $150,000.
- Accounts payable is typically 20% of current year expenses.

A selection of CCC's December 31, 2019 balances are as follows:

Capital Assets	$100,000
Accumulated Depreciation	2,500
Notes Payable	0
Stockholder's Equity	75,500

Prepare a budgeted balance sheet for December 31, 2020.

Charles Cocoa Corporation Budgeted Balance Sheet As at December 31, 2020		
Assets		
Cash		
Accounts Receivable		
Capital Assets		
Accumulated Depreciation		
Total Assets		
Liabilities		
Accounts Payable		
Notes Payable		
Total Liabilities		
Stockholder's Equity		
Total Liabilities and Stockholder's Equity		

AP-15B LO 4 6

a) LimeLemon Inc. is a manufacturer of athletic wear for running and yoga. They sell premium athletic pants. LimeLemon Inc. has a March 30 year end. Estimated sales information for the upcoming fiscal year are as follows:

Month	Sales in Units	Sales Price
April	440	$75/unit
May	520	$75/unit
June	480	$90/unit
July	510	$85/unit
August	300	$85/unit

Prepare the **sales budget** for the first quarter.

LimeLemon Inc. Sales Budget For the Quarter Ended June 30, 2019				
	April	May	June	Period End

b) When creating the budget, management likes to have extra inventory on hand in the event that actual sales are higher than budgeted. Management has determined that 20% of the following month's budgeted sales should be sufficient for the extra inventory. Ending inventory at March 31, 2019 was 100 units.

Prepare the **production budget** for the first quarter.

LimeLemon Inc. Production Budget For the Quarter Ended June 30, 2019				
	April	May	June	Period End

c) Each pair of pants requires 2.5 yards of fabric and each yard costs $12. Management budgets for extra materials in the event that there is a shortage from suppliers. Management would like to have 20% of the following month's production needs in ending inventory each month. Ending inventory of fabric at March 31, 2018 is 300 yards.

Prepare the direct materials budget and purchasing budget for the first quarter.

LimeLemon Inc.
Direct Material Purchases Budget
For the Quarter Ended June 30, 2019

	April	May	June	Period End

LimeLemon Inc.
Purchasing Budget
For the Quarter Ended June 30, 2019

	April	May	June	Period End

d) LimeLemon's sales history indicates that 35% of sales will be for cash and 65% of sales will be on credit. Using the information from the sales budget, the forecasted cash and credit sales can be determined:

LimeLemon Inc.
Forecasted Cash Sales and Credit Sales
For the Quarter Ended June 30, 2019

	April	May	June	Period End

LimeLemon has reviewed past collection history and has determined that credit sales will be collected as follows: 60% is collected in the month of sale and 40% is collected the following month. The total credit sales for the month of March 2019 were $45,000.

Prepare the budgeted schedule of cash receipts for the first quarter.

LimeLemon Inc.
Schedule of Cash Receipts
For the Quarter Ended June 30, 2019

	April	May	June	Period End

e) LimeLemon will pay for 50% of its purchases of material in the month the material is purchased, and the remaining 50% in the following month. The total credit purchases for the month of March 2019 were $25,000.

Prepare the budgeted schedule of cash disbursements for the first quarter.

LimeLemon Inc. Schedule of Cash Disbursements For the Quarter Ended June 30, 2019				
	April	**May**	**June**	**Period End**

f) Prepare a cash budget for the first quarter.

Assume the following:

1) LimeLemon has access to an open line of credit with the bank to borrow money if needed. To keep things simple, ignore interest calculations on the bank borrowings. Also, loan borrowings and repayments are taken in multiples of $1,000.

2) LimeLemon started the year with $11,300 in its bank account and must maintain a minimum cash balance of $4,000 at the end of each month.

3) LimeLemon maintains that it will repay debts as soon as possible with any excess cash that becomes available.

4) LimeLemon has budgeted the following for 2019:
   - Payment for operating expenses = $15,600 for April, $14,300 for May, and $12,500 for June
   - Depreciation expense is $2,500 a month.
   - LimeLemon will need to purchase new equipment costing $38,000. LimeLemon will pay $8,000 in April and the remaining balance in May.
   - Cash dividends of $1,000 will be paid to in all three months of the first quarter.

LimeLemon Inc. Cash Budget For the Quarter Ended June 30, 2019	April	May	June	Period End

AP-16B LO 6

Magnificent Inc. requires a minimum cash balance of $500 at the end of each quarter. Complete the cash budget for Advantage Corp by filling in the grey areas below.

Magnificent Inc. Cash Budget For the Year Ended December 31, 2019	Q1	Q2	Q3	Q4	Period End
Cash (Beginning)	$680				
Cash Receipts:					
Cash from Sales	1,100	1,060			4,690
Collections from Credit Customers		1,440	930		5,955
Total Cash Available	3,355			4,360	11,325
Cash Disbursements:					
Manufacturing Costs		850	650	560	2,785
General and Admin. costs	625	1,100			3,505
Capital Expenditures	875		700		3,750
Dividend Payment	40		440		
Total Cash Disbursements			2,630		10,520
Cash Excess (Deficit)	1,090	340	(520)		
Financing Requirements:					
Loan Borrowings					
Loan Repayments					
Ending Cash Balance _____					

AP-17B LO 1 4

Fast Riders Inc. manufactures and sells plastic bottles to several beverage companies. All plastic bottles produced are identical. At year end (on December 31, 2019), the company gathered the following information to prepare for the 2020 budget.

Materials and Labor Requirements:

Direct materials

- 15 grams of plastic needed per bottle
- $0.001/gram

Direct labor

- 3.6 seconds needed per bottle
- $15/hour

Manufacturing overhead

- DLH as an allocation base
- Predetermined overhead rate = $2.50/DLH

The company expects to sell 20,000,000 bottles in 2020 at an estimated average selling price of $0.10 per bottle. The company uses the weighted average method for inventory flow, and has the following balances in inventory.

Direct Material Inventory (plastic):

- 2020's Beginning inventory for plastic   30,000,000 grams
- 2020's Targeted ending inventory for plastic   20,000,000 grams

Finished Goods Inventory (bottles):

- 2020's Beginning inventory for bottles   3,000,000 bottles
- 2020's Budgeted ending inventory for bottles   2,000,000 bottles

Additional budgeted non-manufacturing expenses for 2020 include:

General and administration costs	$900,000
Insurance	10,000
Utilities	5,000
Interest on loans	1,000

Required

a) Based on the above information, how does Fast Riders benefit from preparing a budget?

_____

_____

_____

_____

b) Prepare the 2020 sales budget (in dollars).

_____

_____

c) Prepare the 2020 production budget (in units).

_____

_____

_____

_____

d) Prepare the direct materials purchasing budget for 2020 (in dollars).

_____

_____

_____

_____

_____

_____

AP-18B LO 4 6

Candice Inc. provides you with the following budgeted information for two months in 2018:

	March	April
Sales	$600,000	$700,000
Manufacturing Costs	200,000	300,000
Capital Expenditures*	300,000	-
General and Administration Costs (including amortization)	70,000	90,000

*includes training programs, machines and buildings

Expectations:

- Cash sales represent 20% of total sales
- All sales on account are collected in the following month
- 50% of March's $300,000 worth of capital expenditures is to be paid at the end of March. The remainder is to be paid in the following month.
- Monthly amortization represents 10% of general and administration costs
- Manufacturing costs and general and administration costs are to be paid in the month in which they are incurred
- Dividends of $5,000 are expected to be declared in March and paid in April
- Candice Inc. obtains the minimum financing needed to ensure at least a $7,000 cash balance at the end of the month through a note payable. Assume that any amount taken out of the note payable may be repaid only at year end.

As of March 1

Cash	$40,000
Accounts Receivable	230,000*
Inventory	35,000
Noncurrent Assets	100,000
Accumulated Depreciation	6,000
Accounts Payable	10,000
Dividends Payable	0
Notes Payable	265,000
Stockholder's Equity	124,000

*Comprised only of sales on account incurred in February

Required

a) What is the difference between a cash budget and an operating budget?

_____

_____

_____

_____

b) Prepare a cash budget for March and April.

Candice Inc. Cash Budget for March and April		
	March	**April**

AP-19B LO 6

Preston Corporation is a manufacturer and distributor of electronic devices. Management has asked you to prepare a cash budget for the upcoming year. The following is the company's budgeted information for the 2020 fiscal year:

	Q1	Q2	Q3	Q4	Period End
Sales (all on credit)	41,600	33,410	44,850	54,340	174,200
Direct Material Purchases	12,480	10,023	13,455	16,302	52,260
Direct Labor	16,640	13,364	17,940	21,736	69,680
Marketing Expense	4,160	3,341	4,485	5,434	17,420
Building Lease Payments	2,080	2,080	2,080	2,080	8,320
Depreciation Expense	4,160	3,341	4,485	5,434	17,420

Additional information is as follows:

- Preston requires ending cash balance for each period to be at a minimum of $12,000. The ending cash balance at Q4-2019 was $12,300.
- All sales are on credit. The collection pattern for sales is 60% in the quarter of sale, 40% in the following quarter.
- There were a total of $15,500 in accounts receivable as at Q4-2019 that is to be collected in full in Q1-2020.
- Purchases of direct materials are paid 50% in the quarter of purchase and 50% in the quarter following the purchase.
- The total direct material purchases in Q4-2019 was $11,000.
- All other expenses will be paid in full in the quarter they are budgeted for.
- Equipment costing a total of $32,000 is to be purchased in the year, half of it will be paid for in Q1, half in Q3.
- Preston has an open line of credit which is used for any borrowings the company may need. Any borrowings are done in multiples of $100.

a) Complete a schedule of cash receipts for the 2020 fiscal year.

	Q1	Q2	Q3	Q4	Period End
Preston Corporation Schedule of Cash Receipts For the Year Ended December 31, 2020					

b)   Prepare a cash budget for the 2020 fiscal year.

	Q1	Q2	Q3	Q4	Period End
Preston Corporation **Cash Budget** **For the Year Ended December 31, 2020**					

Case Study

CS-1

Tom Ato is the President and CEO of a popular chain restaurant-lounge that serves local organic vegetarian dishes throughout the United States. Every year, Tom meets with upper management of Tomayto Restaurant Group at head office, along with his team of accountants in order to establish a budget for the following year. This budget is then rolled out throughout the organization to the separate departments. The departments include: sales and marketing, human resources, accounting and finance, purchasing, and restaurant management.

Recently, Tom has noticed some problems with the effectiveness of his budgets and has hired you, a financial advisor, to help him improve his system.

The budgeting process has always been troublesome for Tom. The departments are very hostile towards each other regarding who gets a stricter budget each year. Lower management does not have any say regarding the budget.

A few years ago, Tom introduced a new incentive program where every manager who was able meet the budget was awarded a bonus based on how much money they saved. Tom always liked to save more because he knows that restaurants are particularly vulnerable in an economic downturn, and he wants to make sure Tomayto survives. He always emphasizes cost savings and managers who were not able to meet the budget do not receive great performance reviews.

When this program was first introduced, he found that many managers were unable to meet the budgeted figures, calling them "unfair" and "impossible." Although the recent business environment has changed drastically, Tomayto still uses a system of incremental budgeting where figures in the budgets are based on prior year's spendings. Over time, the budget has been increased significantly. At the same time, Tom noticed that managers are able to not only meet the figures, but tend to spend exactly the amount of budgeted expenses. He finds this quite odd and has asked you to suggest the reason as to why it could be happening.

At the end of 2018, the company started a new line of restaurants under the name of Potayto. The Potayto project was not accounted for in the budgets for 2018. The Potayto project required working capital of $900,000 upfront to get started. However, Tom realized that he is unable to finance this amount through the cash from the company's accounts. He finds this odd because the company estimated $4,000,000 in net income for 2018. The balance of the cash account at the end of 2017 was $300,000. Note that $5,000,000 was spent in 2018 buying new property for many of the restaurant's stores. Tom wants you to give him a possible reason for why he does not have enough cash on hand despite the large projected net income figure.

Required

1. Address Tom Ato's concerns and highlight some major issues in his budgeting process.
2. Give some suggestions for how Tomayto Restaurant Group's budgetary control system can be made more effective.

Notes

Chapter 8

VARIANCE ANALYSIS AND STANDARD COSTING

LEARNING OBJECTIVES

LO 1 Explain the importance of variance analysis

LO 2 Prepare a static budget and a flexible budget and calculate variances

LO 3 Explain how standard costs are established

LO 4 Calculate quantity and price variances for materials, labor and overhead

LO 5 Calculate quantity and price variances for a service organization

LO 6 Explain ethics in relation to variance analysis

AMEENGAGE Access **ameengage.com** for integrated resources including tutorials, practice exercises, the digital textbook and more.

Assessment Questions

AS-1 LO 1

Explain the concept of management by exception.

_____

_____

AS-2 LO 2

Generally, what is considered a favorable variance? What is considered an unfavorable variance?

_____

_____

_____

AS-3 LO 2

What is a static budget?

_____

_____

_____

AS-4 LO 2

What is a flexible budget?

_____

_____

AS-5 LO 2

How is the flexible budget different from the static budget?

_____

_____

AS-6 LO 2

How is the sales-volume variance calculated?

_____

_____

_____

AS-7 LO 2

How is the flexible budget variance calculated?

_____

_____

_____

AS-8 LO 2

How is the static budget variance calculated?

_____

_____

_____

AS-9 LO 4

When does a price variance occur?

_____

_____

_____

AS-10 LO 3

What is a standard price?

_____

_____

_____

AS-11 LO 3

What is a standard quantity?

_____

_____

AS-12 `LO 4`

Which two components can the flexible budget variance for direct materials and direct labor be broken down into?

_____

_____

_____

AS-13 `LO 4`

How is price variance for direct materials calculated?

_____

_____

_____

AS-14 `LO 4`

What is the formula for quantity variance for direct materials?

_____

_____

AS-15 `LO 4 5`

What is the formula for labor rate variance for direct labor?

_____

_____

_____

AS-16 `LO 4 5`

Explain how to calculate efficiency variance for direct labor.

_____

_____

_____

AS-17 `LO 4 5`

Variable overhead flexible budget variances can be separated into two variances. What are they?

_____

_____

AS-18 `LO 4 5`

Define spending variance.

_____

_____

AS-19 LO 4 5

What is an efficiency variance?

_____

_____

_____

AS-20 LO 6

Do all favorable variances indicate improvements in business operations?

_____

_____

_____

_____

_____

—————————— **Application Questions Group A** ——————————

AP-1A LO 2

Coral Rose is the owner of Rose Flower Shop. In the beginning of the year, she predicted the annual operating income to be $400,000. By the end of the year, she calculated the flexible budget for operating income to be $350,000. Determine the sales-volume variance. Indicate whether the variance is favorable or unfavorable.

_____

_____

_____

AP-2A LO 2

Determine the static-budget variance if there is a favorable sales-volume variance of $200,000 and a favorable flexible budget variance of $50,000. Indicate whether the variance is favorable or unfavorable.

_____

_____

_____

AP-3A LO 2

Determine the flexible budget variance if the sales-volume variance is $100,000 F and static-budget variance is $50,000 U. Indicate whether the variance is favorable or unfavorable.

_____

_____

_____

AP-4A LO 2

If budgeted operating income is $200,000 and actual operating income is $350,000, determine the static budget variance. Indicate whether the variance is favorable or unfavorable.

_____

_____

_____

AP-5A LO 2

Jane Finch held a bake sale yesterday. She sold a total of 500 cookies at $1.00 per cookie. If her budgeted selling price was $1.30, what is her selling-price variance?

_____

_____

AP-6A `LO 4`

Determine the total variance if the price variance is ($800,000) U and the quantity variance is $200,000 F.

_____

_____

AP-7A `LO 4`

Bobby Blue Limited has set the standard price of direct materials to be $0.50 per unit. However, the actual price of input this year was $0.62 per unit. If the company purchased a total of 300,000 units of direct materials, what is the price variance?

_____

_____

AP-8A `LO 4`

Brianna budgeted that she would use 25,000 inches of yarn. She also estimated to make 50 scarves by the end of the year. However, only a total of 40 scarves were knitted during the year. What is the standard quantity of yarn for the actual output?

_____

_____

AP-9A `LO 4`

Lois works at a bakery and is being paid $20 per hour. She normally spends 15 minutes to decorate a cake. However, for this particular week, she spent 20 minutes to decorate a cake. Assume 35 cakes were decorated that week, determine the direct labor efficiency variance per minute.

_____

_____

_____

AP-10A `LO 4`

The standard price for direct materials is $15 per kilogram. If a company purchased 200 kg of direct materials and total cost of these materials was actually $3,200, what is the price variance of the direct materials?

_____

_____

AP-11A `LO 4`

Charles Freedmen Corp. manufactures candles. The standard cost of direct labor is $20/hour, while the standard labor rate is 3 minutes per candle. Consider the following information:

Direct Labor Price Variance	($600) U
Direct Labor Efficiency Variance	$1,000 F
Actual Production for May	4,000 units
Actual Sales	2,500 units

Calculate actual direct labor hours used and actual direct labor rate.

_____

_____

_____

_____

_____

_____

_____

_____

_____

_____

_____

_____

AP-12A LO 4

BagitUP Company manufactures paper bags. Consider the following selected data:

	Direct Materials	**Direct Labor**
Standards per Paper Bag	500 grams of input at $0.01 per gram	0.05 labor hours at $23 per labor hour

Actual Performance:

Paper Bags Produced and Sold	17,000 bags
Direct Materials Purchased and Used	8,130,000 grams
Labor Hours Used	1,500 labor hours
Total Direct Materials Costs	$170,000
Total Direct Labor Costs	$45,200

Required

a) Calculate price variance for direct materials.

_____

_____

_____

_____

b) Provide a possible reason for the favorable or unfavorable price variance for direct materials.

_____

_____

_____

c) Calculate quantity variance for direct materials.

_____

_____

_____

_____

_____

_____

d) Provide a possible reason for the favorable or unfavorable quantity variance for direct materials.

_____

_____

e) Calculate labor rate variance.

_____

_____

_____

_____

_____

f) Provide a possible reason for the favorable or unfavorable rate variance for direct labor.

_____

_____

g) Calculate efficiency variance for direct labor.

_____

_____

_____

_____

_____

h) Provide a possible reason for the favorable or unfavorable efficiency variance for direct labor.

_____

_____

_____

AP-13A LO 4

Robin Luk manufactures carpets. He has two direct cost categories; direct materials and direct labor costs. The allocation of variable manufacturing overhead is based on standard direct labor hours. Robin Luk provides the following information regarding his standards and actual performance for the month of July.

For the month of July, Robin has budgeted 120,000 pounds of direct materials and 50,000 direct labor hours at a total cost of $1,000,000. Based on the 50,000 direct labor hours, the budgeted variable manufacturing overhead was $400,000. The standard cost per pound was $10.65 and the standard quantity per output was 5 pounds.

The following information shows the actual results for the month of July:

Direct Materials

Price Variance	$240,000 F
Price Variance per pound	$2.10 per lb
Efficiency Variance	($90,000) U

Direct Labor:

Labor costs Incurred	$700,000
Efficiency Variance	($20,000) U
Actual Wage Rate – Budgeted Wage Rate	$0.70 per hour

Variable Manufacturing Overhead

Flexible Budget Variance	($15,000) U
Efficiency Variance	($28,700) U

Note: Assume direct materials used are equal to direct materials purchased.

Required

Calculate the following for July:

a)   Total amount of direct materials used.

_____

_____

_____

_____

_____

b)   Variable manufacturing overhead spending variance.

_____

_____

_____

c) Total number of labor hours used.

_____

_____

_____

_____

AP-14A LO 4

Gosslin Manufacturing has two direct cost categories: direct materials and direct labor costs. The company's variable manufacturing overhead is allocated to products based on standard direct labor hours. The following information indicates the standards of Gosslin's manufacturing costs:

Direct Cost Categories:

	Standard Quantity	Cost per Input Unit
Direct Materials	7 pounds per output unit	$10 per pound
Direct Labor	3 hours per output unit	$20 per hour

Manufacturing Overhead:

	Cost per Input Unit
Variable Manufacturing Overhead	$10 per Direct Labor Hour

By the end of May 2019 Gosslin Manufacturing records indicated the following:

Direct materials purchased and used	$12.45 per pound	90,000 pounds
Direct labor	$18 per hour	42,000 labor hours
Total actual variable manufacturing overhead		$340,000
Actual production		13,000 output units

Required

Calculate the following variances.

a) Direct materials price variance.

_____

_____

b) Direct materials quantity variance.

_____

_____

_____

c)   Direct labor rate variance.

_____

_____

d)   Direct labor efficiency variance.

_____

_____

e)   Variable manufacturing overhead spending variance.

_____

_____

f)   Variable manufacturing overhead efficiency variance.

_____

_____

AP-15A LO 2 5

Ace Math Academy provides math help for high school students. The organization believes a small group learning environment allows students to become more comfortable in asking questions while being able to learn from other students. As a result, each instructor is expected to have a class of six students and each session is two hours long. There are four instructors and they are each being paid $35 per hour. Each session is expected to cost $30 for the student. For the month of June, the company expects 120 sessions.

By the end of the month, the company noticed everything has met expectations except the following:

  • Instructors were being paid at $40 per hour
  • There were a total of 100 sessions in the month
  • Students paid $34 per session

Required

a)   Calculate the selling-price variance for the month.

_____

_____

_____

_____

_____

_____

_____

_____

b)   Calculate the rate and efficiency variance per hour for direct labor.

_____

_____

_____

_____

_____

_____

_____

_____

c)   Calculate the total direct labor flexible budget variance.

_____

_____

_____

AP-16A LO 5

TWE Consulting offers professional training programs. There are currently three consultants, Mark Freedman, George Smith and Peter Parkinson. Each consultant costs on average $30 per hour and takes approximately three business days to perform the training program. Assume each program and client is assigned only one consultant. The consultants are expected to work 7.5 hours per business day. Variable overhead costs are based on the amount of consulting hours. The predetermined overhead rate is $13 per consulting hour. For the upcoming period, the company expects 260 training programs. At the end of the period, the company incurred $142,000 in consultants' wages and $42,000 in variable overhead costs. There were 200 training programs and the consultants spent a total of 3,000 consulting hours to train the clients.

Required

a)   Calculate the direct labor rate variance.

_____

_____

_____

_____

_____

_____

b)   Calculate the direct labor efficiency variance.

_____

_____

_____

_____

_____

c) Calculate the variable overhead spending variance.

_____

_____

_____

_____

d) Calculate the variable overhead efficiency variance.

_____

_____

_____

_____

AP-17A LO 2

Fill in the blank cells.

	Actual	Flexible Budget Variance	Flexible Budget	Sales-Volume Variance	Static Budget
Revenue	$220,000			($32,500) U	
Variable Costs			21,315		24,500
Contribution Margin	200,000	3,815 F		(29,315) U	225,500
Fixed Costs		-	77,500	-	
Operating Income	122,500	3,815 F		(29,315) U	148,000
Units Produced and Sold	8,700	-			10,000

AP-18A LO 4

The Chair Company uses a standard costing system when developing its flexible budget amounts. The company produced a total of 2,500 chairs for the year. The following information is related to direct materials:

	Input Purchased and Used	Standard Quantity for Actual Output	Standard Price	Purchase Price
Direct Materials	2,000 sq ft	1 sq ft per chair	$5 per sq ft	$3 per sq ft

Calculate the flexible budget, price and quantity variances for direct materials.

_____

_____

_____

_____
_____
_____
_____
_____
_____
_____
_____
_____
_____

AP-19A LO 2

Using the following information, calculate the static budget, flexible budget and sales-volume variances:

	Actual	Budget
Total Sales Revenue	$400,000	$500,000
Total Direct Materials	100,000	200,000
Total Direct Labor	40,000	35,000
Total Fixed Costs	180,000	180,000
Volume of Production	200,000 units	220,000 units

_____
_____
_____
_____
_____
_____
_____
_____
_____
_____
_____
_____
_____
_____
_____
_____
_____
_____
_____

AP-20A LO 2

VroomVroom Company manufactures car parts. The budgeted operating income is $1,500,000 at the end of 2019. However, the actual operating income totaled to only $900,000. Assume the actual and budgeted production is the same.

Required

a)   What is the total static budget variance?

_____

_____

_____

_____

b)   Assume the flexible budget operating income was $800,000. Determine total sales-volume variance.

_____

_____

_____

_____

c)   Refer to part b), and determine the total flexible budget variance.

_____

_____

_____

_____

Application Questions Group B

AP-1B LO 2

Samantha Beadle is the owner of MultiMedia Advertising Company. In the beginning of the year, she predicted the annual operating income to be $412,000. By the end of the year, she calculated the flexible budget for operating income to be $427,000. Determine the sales-volume variance. Indicate whether the variance is favorable or unfavorable.

_____

_____

AP-2B LO 2

Determine the static-budget variance if there is a favorable sales-volume variance of $115,000 and an unfavorable flexible budget variance of $18,000. Indicate whether the variance is favorable or unfavorable.

_____

_____

_____

AP-3B LO 2

Determine the flexible budget variance if the sales-volume variance is $10,000 F and static-budget variance is ($6,000) U. Indicate whether the variance is favorable or unfavorable.

_____

_____

_____

AP-4B LO 2

If budgeted operating income is $1,210,000 and actual operating income is $1,335,000, determine the static budget variance. Indicate whether the variance is favorable or unfavorable.

_____

_____

AP-5B LO 2

John Brinch held a bake sale yesterday. He sold a total of 176 cookies at $1.25 per cookie. If his budgeted selling price was $1.30, what is his selling-price variance?

_____

_____

_____

AP-6B LO 4

Determine the total variance if the price variance is $800,000 F and the quantity variance is ($200,000) U.

_____

_____

AP-7B LO 4

Bella Buler Company has set the standard price of direct materials to be $0.62 per unit. However, the actual price of input this year was $0.50 per unit. If the company purchased a total of 222,000 units of direct materials, what is the price variance?

AP-8B LO 4

Taylor budgeted that she would use 15,000 inches of yarn. She also estimated to make 40 scarves by the end of the year. However, only a total of 35 scarves were knitted during the year. What is the standard quantity of yarn for the actual output?

AP-9B LO 4

Lonnie works at a bakery and is being paid $15 per hour. She normally spends 10 minutes to decorate a cake. However, for this particular week, she spent 15 minutes to decorate each cake. Assuming 38 cakes were decorated that week, determine the direct labor efficiency variance per minute.

AP-10B LO 4

The standard price for direct materials is $13 per pound. If a company purchased 235 pounds of direct materials and total cost of these materials was actually $3,100, what is the price variance of the direct materials?

AP-11B LO 4

Candle's Corp. manufactures sandals. The standard cost of direct labor is $15/hour, while the standard labor rate is 10 minutes per pair of sandals. Consider the following information:

Direct Labor Rate Variance	($840) U
Direct Labor Efficiency Variance	$1,200 F
Actual Production for May	3,000 units
Actual Sales	2,500 units

Calculate actual direct labor hours used and actual direct labor rate. Calculate the overall labor variance. Explain what factors may have contributed to the rate, efficiency and overall labor variances.

_____
_____
_____
_____
_____
_____
_____
_____
_____
_____
_____
_____
_____
_____
_____
_____
_____
_____

AP-12B LO 4

Bottoms UP Company manufactures recyclable bottles. Consider the following selected data:

	Direct Materials	**Direct Labor**
Standards per Bottle	450 oz of input at $0.015/oz	0.075 labor hours at $21/labor hour

Actual Performance:

Bottles Produced and Sold	17,000 units
Direct Materials Purchased and Used	7,150,000 oz
Labor Hours Used	1,400 labor hours
Total Direct Materials Costs	$100,100
Total Direct Labor Costs	$27,650

Required

a) Calculate price variance for direct materials.

_____
_____
_____

b) Provide a possible reason for the favorable or unfavorable price variance for direct materials.

_____
_____

c) Calculate quantity variance for direct materials.

_____
_____
_____
_____

d) Provide a possible reason for the favorable or unfavorable quantity variance for direct materials.

_____

_____

e) Calculate labor rate variance.

_____

_____

_____

f) Provide a possible reason for the favorable or unfavorable rate variance for direct labor.

_____

_____

g) Calculate efficiency variance for direct labor.

_____

_____

_____

_____

h) Provide a possible reason for the favorable or unfavorable efficiency variance for direct labor.

_____

_____

AP-13B LO 4

Ruk Corporation manufactures nightstands. The company has two direct cost categories; direct materials and direct labor costs. The allocation of variable manufacturing overhead is based on standard direct labor hours. Ruk provides the following information regarding its standards and actual performance for the month of July.

For the month of July, Ruk has budgeted 480,000 pounds of direct materials and 45,000 direct labor hours at a total cost of $967,500. Based on the 45,000 direct labor hours, the budgeted variable manufacturing overhead was $360,000. The standard cost per pound was $11.25 and the standard quantity per output was 25 pounds.

The following information shows the actual results for the month of July:

Direct Materials

Price Variance	$90,400 F
Price Variance per Pound	$0.19 per lb
Efficiency Variance	$45,000 F

Direct Labor

Labor Costs Incurred	$1,005,000
Efficiency Variance	$5,912 F
Actual Wage Rate – Budgeted Wage Rate	$0.97 per hour

Variable Manufacturing Overhead

Flexible Budget Variance	($17,800) U
Efficiency Variance	($25,900) U

Required

Calculate the following for July:

a) Total amount of direct materials used.

b) Variable manufacturing overhead spending variance.

c) Total number of labor hours used.

AP-14B LO 4

Champlain Manufacturing has two direct cost categories: direct materials and direct labor costs. The company's variable manufacturing overhead is allocated to products based on standard direct labor hours. The following information indicates the standards of Champlain's manufacturing costs:

Direct Cost Categories		
	Standard Quantity	**Cost per Input Unit**
Direct Materials	7.5 pounds per output unit	$11.25 per pound
Direct Labor	0.3 hours per output unit	$22 per hour

Manufacturing Overhead	
	Cost per Input Unit
Variable Manufacturing Overhead	$9.50 per Direct Labor Hour

By the end of May 2019 Champlain Manufacturing records indicated the following:

Direct materials purchased and used	$10.95 per pound	92,000 pounds
Direct labor	$22.50 per hour	4,350 labor hours
Total actual variable manufacturing overhead		$32,750
Actual production		13,000 output units

Required

Calculate the following variances.

a) Direct materials price variance.

_____

_____

b) Direct materials quantity variance.

_____

_____

_____

c) Direct labor rate variance.

_____

_____

d) Direct labor efficiency variance.

_____

_____

e) Variable manufacturing overhead spending variance.

_____

_____

_____

f) Variable manufacturing overhead efficiency variance.

_____

_____

_____

_____

_____

AP-15B LO 2 5

Old Town Academy provides music lessons for middle school students. The organization believes a small group learning environment is crucial for learning music. As a result, each instructor is expected to have a class of five students and each session is two hours long. There are four instructors and each one is paid $37.50 per hour. Each session is expected to cost $32 for the student. For the month of June, the company expects 120 sessions.

By the end of the month, the company noticed everything has met expectations except the following:

- Instructors were being paid $45 per hour
- There were a total of 130 sessions in the month
- Students paid $37.50 per session

Required

a) Calculate the selling-price variance for the month.

_____

_____

_____

_____

b) Calculate the rate and efficiency variance for direct labor.

_____

_____

_____

_____

_____

_____

c) Calculate the total direct labor flexible budget variance.

_____

_____

_____

_____

_____

_____

_____

_____

_____

_____

AP-16B LO 5

DSC Consulting offers social media marketing training programs. There are currently three consultants that on average earn $45 per hour. The consultants are expected to work 8 hours per business day. Each training program takes approximately three business days to perform and is taught by one consultant per program. Variable overhead costs are based on the amount of consulting hours. The predetermined overhead rate is $14.50 per consulting hour. For the upcoming period, the company expects 265 training programs. At the end of the period, the company incurred $220,500 in consultants' wages and $57,750 in variable overhead costs. There were 240 training programs offered and the consultants spent a total of 5,250 consulting hours to train the clients.

Required

a) Calculate the direct labor rate variance.

b) Calculate the direct labor efficiency variance.

c) Calculate the variable overhead spending variance.

d) Calculate the variable overhead efficiency variance.

AP-17B LO 2

Fill in the blank cells.

	Actual	Flexible Budget Variance	Flexible Budget	Sales-Volume Variance	Static Budget
Revenue	$325,000			($12,500) U	
Variable Costs			61,315		62,250
Contribution Margin	257,500	(18,685) U		(11,565) U	287,750
Fixed Costs		-	127,500	-	
Operating Income	130,000	(18,685) U		(11,565) U	160,250
Units Produced and Sold	9,250	-			9,100

AP-18B LO 4

The Sherry Company uses a standard costing system when developing its flexible budget amounts. The company produced a total of 3,500 units for the year. The following information is related to direct materials:

	Input Purchased and Used	Standard Quantity for Actual Output	Standard Price	Purchase Price
Direct Materials	4,725 sq ft	1.25 sq ft per chair	$5 per sq ft	$3.50 per sq ft

Calculate the flexible budget, price and quantity variances for direct materials.

_____

_____

_____

_____

_____

_____

_____

_____

_____

_____

_____

AP-19B LO 2

Using the following information, calculate the static budget, flexible budget and sales-volume variances:

	Actual	Budget
Total Sales Revenue	$270,000	$275,000
Total Direct Materials	112,000	137,500
Total Direct Labor	27,500	15,000
Total Fixed Costs	90,000	90,000
Volume of Production	175,200 units	172,000 units

_____
_____
_____
_____
_____
_____
_____
_____
_____
_____
_____

AP-20B LO 2

Smashup Company manufactures video games. The budgeted operating income is $1,625,000 at the end of 2018. Actual operating income totaled $1,900,000. Assume the actual and budgeted production is the same.

Required

a) What is the total static-budget variance?

_____
_____
_____

b) Assume the flexible budget operating income was $1,775,000. Determine total sales-volume variance.

_____
_____

c) Refer to part b), determine the total flexible budget variance.

_____
_____
_____
_____
_____
_____
_____
_____
_____
_____
_____
_____

Critical Thinking

CT-1 LO  1 2 3 4 6

Mattle Manufacturing specializes in contemporary furniture. The production involves three departments: purchasing, shaping and assembling. The purchasing department buys the materials for company use and must consider the price, quality, availability and reliability when choosing suppliers and merchandise. The shaping department obtains materials from the material storage, and then carefully cuts and shapes the materials for the assembling department. Lastly, the assembling department puts the pieces together.

Every quarter, Mattle Manufacturing evaluates the three departments. The performance evaluation simply compares the overall departments' manufacturing costs with the budgeted amounts. For the past four performance evaluations, the purchasing division always exceeded the company's expectations. Although the assembling department did not perform as well as the purchasing division, it has shown some improvements. However, the shaping department's performance evaluation has always been disappointing. Their last performance report showed a staggering unfavorable manufacturing cost variance of $550,000. Due to the continuous poor performance, the controller decided to investigate the cost problems in the shaping department.

The controller conducted an interview with the manager. During the interview, the manager of the shaping department was asked to explain their poor performance. The manager replied:

"I know that our department has been showing poor results for the past four performance evaluations. However, our department has been working really hard to meet our budgets. In fact, we've been experiencing many difficulties lately. The materials that we requested were difficult to cut or shape into certain forms because they get chipped so easily. As a result, we have spent a lot of time scraping work and sorting material that can actually be shaped."

Assume you are the controller of Mattle Manufacturing. What kind of information would you need to verify the shaping department manager's response? Explain how you would utilize the information.

_____

_____

_____

_____

_____

_____

_____

_____

_____

_____

_____

_____

_____

_____

_____

_____

_____

Notes

Chapter 9

PERFORMANCE EVALUATION IN DECENTRALIZED ORGANIZATIONS

LEARNING OBJECTIVES

LO 1 Explain the different types of responsibility centers

LO 2 Explain the concept of segment reporting

LO 3 Differentiate between traceable and common fixed costs in segment reporting

LO 4 Describe joint costs and methods of joint cost allocation

LO 5 Apply support cost allocation

LO 6 Evaluate the performance of investment centers using return on investment and residual income

LO 7 Explain ethical considerations related to performance goals

Appendix

LO 8 Explain the concept and apply the different types of transfer pricing

AMEENGAGE™ *Access **ameengage.com** for integrated resources including tutorials, practice exercises, the digital textbook and more.*

—————— Assessment Questions ——————

AS-1 LO 1

In a decentralized organization, who has the power to make decisions?

AS-2 LO 1

Define autonomy.

AS-3 LO 1

How does a decentralized organization promote autonomy?

AS-4 LO 1

Define responsibility center.

_____

_____

_____

AS-5 LO 1

What is responsibility accounting?

_____

_____

_____

AS-6 LO 1

What are the different types of responsibility centers?

_____

_____

_____

AS-7 LO 1

What does the manager of a cost center control?

_____

_____

_____

AS-8 LO 1

What is a revenue center responsible for?

_____

_____

_____

AS-9 LO 1

What is a profit center accountable for?

_____

_____

_____

AS-10 LO 1

How are investment centers evaluated?

_____

_____

AS-11 [LO 2]

In accounting, what does a segment mean?

_____

_____

_____

AS-12 [LO 2]

What is segment reporting?

_____

_____

_____

AS-13 [LO 2]

What is a segment margin?

_____

_____

_____

AS-14 [LO 2]

How is the segment margin percentage calculated?

_____

_____

_____

AS-15 [LO 3]

What does the segment margin percentage indicate?

_____

_____

_____

AS-16 [LO 3]

What are traceable fixed costs?

_____

_____

AS-17 `LO` `3`

If a company decides to remove a particular segment, how will the segment's traceable fixed cost be treated?

_____

_____

_____

AS-18 `LO` `3`

What is a common fixed cost?

_____

_____

_____

AS-19 `LO` `4`

What is a joint cost? Provide an example of an industry that would have joint costs.

_____

_____

_____

AS-20 `LO` `4`

Describe how the physical measurement method allocates joint costs and when this method would be best used.

_____

_____

_____

AS-21 `LO` `4`

Describe how the relative sales value method allocates joint costs and when this method would be best used.

_____

_____

_____

AS-22 `LO` `4`

Describe how the net realizable value method allocates joint costs and when this method would be best used.

_____

_____

_____

AS-23 LO 5

What is a support cost? Provide some examples of support costs.

_____

_____

_____

AS-24 LO 5

How does the direct method allocate support costs to production departments?

_____

_____

AS-25 LO 6

What are two performance evaluation measures that can be used for investment centers?

_____

_____

_____

AS-26 LO 6

What information does return on investment provide?

_____

_____

_____

AS-27 LO 6

What does residual income measure?

_____

_____

_____

AS-28 LO 8

Define transfer price.

_____

_____

_____

AS-29 LO 8

Define transfer pricing.

_____

_____

_____

AS-30 `LO 8`

What is a market price?

_____

_____

AS-31 `LO 8`

What does it mean when there is an intermediate market for a particular product?

_____

_____

_____

AS-32 `LO 8`

Under the market-based approach, how do companies set their transfer prices?

_____

_____

AS-33 `LO 8`

How is a transfer price determined if the cost-based transfer price approach is used?

_____

_____

_____

AS-34 `LO 8`

What is a negotiated transfer price?

_____

_____

AS-35 `LO 8`

Define the range of acceptable transfer prices.

_____

_____

_____

AS-36 `LO 8`

Using the negotiated transfer price approach, what would be the selling division's minimum selling price if there is idle capacity?

_____

_____

AS-37 LO 8

Using the negotiated transfer price approach, what would be considered in the selling division's minimum selling price if there is no idle capacity?

AS-38 LO 8

When deciding whether to purchase a product from another division, what would be considered as the purchasing division's maximum price?

————————— **Application Questions Group A** —————————

AP-1A LO 1 2

Mulan Medium Inc. manufactures and sells blank CDs and DVDs in Canada and the United States. The company has two levels of segments. The first level is segmented by country and the second level is segmented by product type. Assume you were given only the following information.

For the past year, total sales for Mulan Medium totaled $1,000,000. The sales in Canada totaled $600,000. 70% of the sales in the United States were related to CDs. The selling price for a blank CD and blank DVD is $1.50 and $2.50 respectively.

Required

a) Prepare a hierarchy of segments for Mulan Medium.

b) How many units of DVDs were sold in the US in the past year?

_____

_____

_____

_____

AP-2A LO 1 2

Match the following terms with the correct definition in the table below.

List of possible terms:

- Segment
- Responsibility center
- Responsibility accounting

- Autonomy
- Decentralized organization

Term (fill in)	Definition
	A system that measures the plans and actual performance of each area of a department.
	A part of a company for which there is separate data regarding cost, revenue, or profit.
	The right or power to govern oneself without external control and constraint.
	An entity in which the power to make decisions is not solely held by a few top managers or executives, but also held by lower level employees.
	A department for which a manager is held accountable for performance.

AP-3A LO 2

Conway Phones Inc. sells one type of home phone and one type of cellular phone. Revenue and cost information for the year ended December 31, 2019 relating to the products are presented below.

	Product	
	Home Phones	Cell Phones
Selling price per phone	$50	$75
Variable cost per phone	25	40
Traceable fixed costs	150,000	100,000

The company incurs $180,000 in common fixed costs per year. Conway Phones manufactured and sold 20,000 home phones and 25,000 cell phones.

Prepare a segmented contribution margin statement for the year based on product line.

Conway Phones Inc. **Segmented Contribution Margin Statement** **For the Year Ended December 31, 2019**			
		Segment (Product Line)	
	Total	Home Phones	Cell Phones

AP-4A LO 2 3

Swelter Electronics Company (Swelter) sells its electronic products through two segments based on geographic markets: North America and Europe. Revenue and cost information prepared by Swelter's accountant for the past year relating to the markets are presented below.

	Market	
	North America	Europe
Sales	$600,000	$850,000
Variable cost	350,000	500,000
Traceable fixed costs	200,000	270,000
Common fixed costs	250,000	

Required

a) Which market had the highest segment margin in the past year?

b) Which market had the highest segment margin percentage in the past year?

c) Should Swelter's accountant allocate the common fixed costs to the two segments? Explain.

AP-5A LO 4

Master Company processes a raw material that produces two joint products – Magna and Delta. At split-off, Magna can be sold for $5.00 per pound and Delta can be sold for $7.00 per pound. It costs $90 to produce a batch of Magna and Delta. Each batch contains 14 pounds of Magna and 6 pounds of Delta.

Required

a) Allocate the joint cost of producing Magna and Delta using the physical measurement method.

b) Allocate the joint cost of producing Magna and Delta ore using the relative sales value method.

c) The sales manager has advised that a batch of 6 pounds of Delta can be processed further at an additional cost of $20. With this additional processing, the 6 pounds of Delta can be sold for $9.00 a pound. Allocate the $90 cost to Magna and Delta using the net realizable value method if Delta is processed further.

d) Based on the information in part c), should Master Company process the Delta further?

AP-6A 5

Ruby Company has two support departments – Maintenance and Power. These departments provide services to the two manufacturing departments – Division A and Division B. Ruby Company uses the direct method to allocate support department costs to the manufacturing divisions based on the number of service hours. The following is a summary of the planned level of activities for the past year.

	Division A	Division B	Total Hours	Total Fixed Costs
Maintenance	900	1,800	2,700	$125,000.00
Power	23,000	14,000	37,000	$215,000.00

For example, Maintenance planned on supplying 900 hours of service to Division A and 1,800 hours of service to Division B. The total fixed costs in Maintenance and Power were $125,000 and $215,000, respectively. Ruby Company allocates the fixed costs of the support departments using the planned level of activity. The following is a summary of the actual level of activity for the past year.

	Division A	Division B	Total Hours	Total Cost
Maintenance	1,200	1,400	2,600	$85,000.00
Power	22,000	16,000	38,000	$60,000.00

For example, Power provided 22,000 hours of service to Division A and 16,000 hours of service to Division B. The total variable costs in Maintenance and Power were $85,000 and $60,000, respectively. Ruby Company allocates the variable costs of the support departments using the actual level of activity. Allocate the support costs to Division A and Division B using the direct method.

	Division A	Division B	Total Cost

AP-7A LO 6

Kim Seating owns a small convenience store and gas bar. Total average business assets in the most recent year amount to $1,500,000. Liabilities total $600,000 and owners' equity total $900,000. The land, on which the business is located, is carried at a historical cost of $150,000. In the past year the business income was $250,000

When it was originally built the business was located in a rural area outside a large city. Since then the city has expanded and the business is surrounded by office and residential towers. Kim was recently offered $3,000,000 for her business. The developer wants to tear down the business and build a large condominium apartment building on the property.

Required

a)   Calculate the ROI for this business.

b) Kim expects a minimum return of 12% on this business. Calculate the residual income.

_____

_____

c) Kim's business advisor has argued that ROI should be calculated based on the value of the business. Calculate the ROI for this business assuming that the business is valued at $3,000,000.

_____

_____

d) Calculate the residual income if the value of the business is taken as $3,000,000.

_____

_____

e) Comment on these results.

_____

_____

_____

AP-8A LO 2 6

Magnet Systems Inc. is a software company with two locations: one in the east and one in the west. The head office is located right in the middle of the two locations. The revenue and cost information for the year ended May 31, 2019, are presented below.

	Segment (Location)	
	East	**West**
Selling price per unit	$85	$80
Variable costs per unit	$60	$50
Traceable fixed costs	$400,000	$250,000
Average Total Assets	$5,000,000	$4,000,000
Required Return	15%	10%

Magnet Systems East sold 40,000 units during the year while Magnet Systems West sold 25,000. The company incurs $325,000 in common fixed costs per year.

Required

a) Prepare a segmented contribution margin statement for the year ended May 31, 2019.

Magnet Systems Inc. Segmented Contribution Margin Statement For the Year Ended May 31, 2019			
		Segment (Location)	
	Total	East	West

b) Calculate the ROI of each segment. Which segment was more profitable during the year?

_____

_____

_____

_____

_____

c) Calculate the residual income of each segment.

_____

_____

_____

_____

AP-9A LO 3 6

The North American segment of Marvin Inc. had the following information gathered from its fiscal year end financial reports at November 30, 2019.

Average Total Assets	$420,000
Operating Income	$50,000
Sales	$225,000
Required Return	10%

Required

a) Calculate the segment margin percentage for the North American segment.

_____

b) Calculate the return on investment for the North American segment.

_____

c) Calculate the residual income for the North American segment.

_____

AP-10A [LO 8]

A company is divided into two segments: Segment A and Segment B. Segment B wants to purchase 2,000 units of the goods produced in Segment A. The company has a policy of using cost based transfer pricing. Normally, transfer price is determined by adding a 25% increase on cost. The following costs pertain to the products produced in Segment A:

	Per Unit	Total (2,000 units)
Direct materials	$15	
Direct labor	$12	
Variable manufacturing overhead	$9	
Fixed manufacturing overhead		$8,000
Selling, general and administrative costs		$10,000

a) What is the transfer price charged to a unit sold by Segment A to Segment B if variable cost is used as the cost base?

b) What is the transfer price charged to a unit sold by Segment A to Segment B if full cost is used as the cost base?

AP-11A [LO 8]

Starnot Construction Inc. has a steel division that produces and sells blocks of steel. The following information pertains to each block of steel.

Selling price on outside market	$20
Variable manufacturing cost per unit	$11
Fixed costs per unit	$4

The company also has a construction division that could use these blocks of steel as material for their construction projects. The construction division is currently purchasing 100,000 blocks of steel annually from an external supplier at a cost of $18 per unit. The steel division has sufficient idle capacity to fulfill a potential transfer of goods to the construction division. Starnot Construction only utilizes negotiated transfer prices.

Determine the range of acceptable transfer prices for the blocks of steel between the two divisions (if such a range exists). Explain your reasoning.

_____

_____

_____

_____

Application Questions Group B

AP-1B LO 3

Triston Aim Software develops and sells two types of software: computer games and information technology (IT) software. The company is segmented based on these two product lines. The company has three offices: an office dedicated to the development and sales of computer games, one for the development and sales of IT software, and the head office. The head office is owned outright, while the other two offices are rented. Advertising campaigns have always sold the company as a whole as opposed to the separate segments. Indicate whether each of the following fixed costs is traceable or common.

Traceable or Common?	Fixed Cost
	Facility rent
	Advertising
	Depreciation of equipment used to develop software
	Salary of the company's CEO
	Salary of computer game developers
	Fee paid to accounting firm that performs companywide audit

AP-2B LO 8

Match the following terms with the correct definition in the table below.

List of possible terms:

- Transfer price
- Negotiated transfer price
- Transfer pricing
- Market price
- Intermediate market

Term (fill in)	Definition
	The price normally charged for a similar product to an external consumer
	The practice that focuses on how companies price goods or services transferred between a company's segments
	A competitive outside market for a similar product
	The price one division charges for a good or service sold to another division within the company
	A transfer price *mutually agreed* upon between the buying and selling divisions

AP-3B LO 2 3

Constantino Appliances Ltd. manufactures and sells kitchen appliances. The most recent monthly contribution margin statement for the entire company is shown below.

Sales	$580,000
Less: variable costs	265,000
Contribution margin	315,000
Less: fixed costs	415,000
Operating income (loss)	($100,000)

The CEO is starting to worry because company has shown a loss for the past several months. In an attempt to identify the specific area of concern, the CEO has asked the accountant to prepare a contribution margin statement segmented by its three different primary sales channels: online, retail, and catalogue. The accountant has developed the following data:

	Sales Channel		
	Online	**Retail**	**Catalogue**
Sales	$200,000	$150,000	$230,000
Variable costs as a % of sales	45%	40%	50%
Traceable fixed costs	$75,000	$82,000	$109,000

Required

a) Prepare a segmented contribution margin statement for the year based on sales channel.

<table>
<tr><td colspan="5" align="center">Constantino Appliances Ltd.
Segmented Contribution Margin Statement (Past Month)</td></tr>
<tr><td></td><td></td><td colspan="3" align="center">Segment (Sales Channel)</td></tr>
<tr><td></td><td align="center">Total</td><td align="center">Online</td><td align="center">Retail</td><td align="center">Catalogue</td></tr>
<tr><td></td><td></td><td></td><td></td><td></td></tr>
<tr><td></td><td></td><td></td><td></td><td></td></tr>
<tr><td></td><td></td><td></td><td></td><td></td></tr>
<tr><td></td><td></td><td></td><td></td><td></td></tr>
<tr><td></td><td></td><td></td><td></td><td></td></tr>
<tr><td></td><td></td><td></td><td></td><td></td></tr>
<tr><td></td><td></td><td></td><td></td><td></td></tr>
<tr><td></td><td></td><td></td><td></td><td></td></tr>
</table>

b) The sales manager of Constantino Appliances thinks that sales in the retail market would increase by 20% if they spend $15,000 on advertising in each period. Assuming his prediction is accurate, would you recommend increasing the costs of advertising?

_____

_____

_____

_____

c) Assume that the retail segment can be divided into another level of segments based on geographic regions: Eastern, Central and Western. Is it true that the sum of the traceable fixed costs for each of the three geographic regions always has to equal the total traceable fixed costs related to the retail sales channel?

_____

_____

_____

_____

AP-4B LO 4

Rocky Mining (RM) operates a gold mine. On average, RM mines 4 tons of ore to yield one ounce of gold and 128,000 ounces of rock as by-product. RM spends $1,000 to mine one ounce of gold and receives $1,100 per ounce of gold. The ore from which the gold is salvaged is sold to customers who crush the ore to sell as road fill and landscaping material. The average amount RM receives for 128,000 ounces of rock is $240.

Required

a) Allocate the cost of mining an ounce of gold to the gold and the ore using the physical measurement method.

_____

_____

_____

_____

_____

b) Allocate the cost of mining an ounce of gold to the gold and the ore using the relative sales value method.

_____

_____

_____

_____

AP-5B LO 4

Fox Company processes a chemical that yields two joint products – Clean and Wash. Each batch costs $1,000 and produces 30 gallons of Clean and 40 gallons of Wash. Both products need additional processing after the initial split-off.

Clean is processed further at a cost of $2.50 per gallon. Wash is processed further at a cost of $2.25 per gallon. Clean and Wash can be sold for $22 and $19 per gallon, respectively.

Management at Fox Company does not like the joint cost allocation results of the net realized value method. They want you to undertake a cost allocation so that the gross margin percent (revenue minus gross margin divided by revenue) is the same. Senior management feels that this will result in a better distribution of the joint cost.

Required

a) Allocate the $1,000 joint cost using the net realizable value method.

	Clean	Wash	Total

b) Allocate the $1,000 joint cost of each batch so that the gross margin percent of the two products is the same.

	Clean	Wash	Total

AP-6B LO 2 5

The Finance Department at Mark Company produced the following segment margin statement for the most recent period.

	Division A	Division B	Total
Revenue	$1,200,000	$2,400,000	$3,600,000
Variable Costs	650,000	125,000	775,000
Contribution Margin	$550,000	$2,275,000	$2,825,000
Allocated Fixed Costs	500,000	1,000,000	1,500,000
Segment Margin	$50,000	$1,275,000	$1,325,000

Fixed costs were allocated to the two divisions based on each division's share of total revenue. For example the fixed cost allocated to Division A was ($1,200,000/$3,600,000) × $1,500,000.

The company president has just returned from a course where she heard about the notion of traceable fixed costs and common fixed costs. Upon investigation it was determined that only $200,000 of fixed costs were truly common costs. A further $1,000,000 of fixed costs were traceable: $200,000 to Division A and $800,000 to Division B. Finally, $300,000 of fixed costs were support costs that should be attributed to Division A and Davison B based on each division's share of total revenue.

Recast the above exhibit to reflect the additional information provided about fixed costs.

	Division A	Division B	Total

AP-7B LO 2 3 6

Disc Electronics splits its operations into two divisions - hardware and software. The hardware division can be further segmented by product line as shown:

	Segment		
	Hardware		**Software**
	Components	**Accessories**	
Selling price per unit	$120	$35	$50
Variable costs per unit	$90	$20	$20
Traceable fixed costs	$900,000	$300,000	$800,000
Average Total Assets	$3,000,000	$1,600,000	$2,000,000
Required Return	12%	12%	30%
Yearly Sales	40,000	30,000	50,000

Disc Electronics had common fixed costs of $200,000.

Required

a) Prepare a segmented contribution margin statement for the year ended August 31, 2019.

Disc Electronics Segmented Contribution Margin Statement For the Year Ended August 31, 2019				
		Hardware		Software
	Total	Components	Accessories	

b) Calculate the segment margin percentage for each segment.

_____

_____

_____

c) Calculate the ROI of each segment. Which segment was more profitable during the year?

_____

_____

_____

_____

d) Calculate the residual income of each segment

_____

_____

_____

_____

AP-8B LO 2 6

Depp Shipping Inc. provides long-distance freight services. They provide shipping by truck and by train and track each method separately in segments. Sales prices are based on kilograms being shipped in order to provide a good comparison between segments. Below is the information regarding each shipping segment for the year.

	Segment	
	Truck	Train
Selling price per kg	$12	$20
Variable costs per kg	$7	$16
Traceable fixed costs	$1,200,000	$2,100,000
Average Total Assets	$7,000,000	$12,000,000
Required Return	12%	12%
Total kilograms shipped	420,000	780,000

The company incurs $200,000 in common fixed costs per year.

Required

a) Prepare a segmented contribution margin statement for the year ended May 31, 2019.

Depp Shipping Inc. Segmented Contribution Margin Statement For the Year Ended December 31, 2019			
		Segment	
	Total	Truck	Train

b) Calculate the ROI of each segment. Which segment was more profitable during the year?

c) Calculate the residual income of each segment.

AP-9B LO 3 6

The Hardware Department of Trillian Inc. had the following information gathered from their fiscal year end financial reports at December 31, 2019.

Average Total Assets	$1,325,000
Operating Income	$215,000
Required Return	12%
Sales	$1,350,000

Required

a) Calculate the segment margin percentage for the Hardware Department.

b) Calculate the return on investment for the Hardware Department.

c) Calculate the residual income for the Hardware Department.

AP-10B LO 8

The bottling department of Landry Drinks Inc. manufactures and sells bottles that can be sold either to the beverage department within the company or to external customers. Each bottle produced by the bottling department has a selling price of $1.50 on the outside market and a variable manufacturing cost of $0.50. The beverage department currently purchases the bottles for its beverages from an outside supplier at a cost of $1.25 per bottle. The bottling department is currently operating at capacity. The company policy states that any internal purchases can be negotiated among the two departments.

Required

a) Determine the range of acceptable transfer prices for the bottles (if such a range exists). Explain your reasoning.

b) Assume that the outside selling price of a bottle produced by the bottling department includes $0.25 to account for the cost of shipping. The cost of shipping will not be incurred by the bottling department on any internal transfers. What is the transfer price that will be agreed upon by the two departments, if any?

_____

_____

_____

_____

_____

AP-11B LO 8

Aimerson Technology Company's audio division produces high-quality computer speakers. Aimerson has a computer division that wants to deliver computers and speakers as part of its package to consumers. Therefore, the computer division is considering purchasing computer speakers from the company's audio division. Consider the following information provided by the company's accountant.

Audio Division (Seller):

Production capacity per year	200,000	speaker sets
Variable manufacturing cost per unit	$16	per speaker set
Selling costs per unit (commission and shipping)	$7	per speaker set
Fixed overhead costs per year (when producing at capacity)	$1,000,000	
Selling price of speaker set charged to outside customers*	$42	per speaker set

Computer Division (Purchaser):

Cost of buying identical speaker set from external supplier	$38	per speaker set
Required number of speaker sets per year	70,000	speaker sets

*Includes selling costs

Required

a) Is it feasible in this case to use market prices to set the internal transfer price of the speakers?

_____

_____

_____

_____

b) Assume that the company uses cost-based transfer pricing and has a policy of using absorption costing. What is the transfer price that the audio division will charge the computer division on the internal transfer (assuming no percentage increase is applied to the cost)?

_____

_____

_____

c) Assume that the company uses negotiated transfer prices and the audio division is currently producing 120,000 speaker sets annually. What is the acceptable range of transfer prices, if any?

_____

_____

_____

_____

_____

d) Assume that the company uses negotiated transfer prices and the audio division is currently producing 200,000 speaker sets annually. For internal transfers, selling costs are not incurred by the audio division . What is the acceptable range of transfer prices, if any?

_____

_____

_____

_____

_____

Case Study

CS-1 LO 2 3 8

Ronin Bike Company manufactures two types of products for children: bicycles and bicycle helmets. Ronin produces only one model of each product. Each product is manufactured in a separate factory, and each factory is leased by the company. The following revenue and cost information was provided to the company's CEO for last month (the month ended January 31, 2019).

	Product Line	
	Bicycle	**Helmet**
Sales	$300,000	$150,000
Variable cost of goods sold as a percentage of sales	40%	35%
Traceable fixed manufacturing overhead costs	$55,000	$42,000
Traceable fixed selling, general, and administrative expenses	$27,000	$16,000

All sales during the month were made to outside customers. Each month, the volume produced is equal to the volume sold for both segments. In January, 2,000 bikes and 7,500 helmets were sold. All fixed manufacturing overhead costs are traceable to the segments. Common fixed selling, general and administrative expenses totaled $32,000. Sales commissions were paid in the amount of $9/unit for bikes and $1.50/unit for helmets. Each product's selling price included an increase equal to the sales commission amount. Sales commissions are only applied on sales to outside customers. Sales commission is the only variable selling, general and administrative (SG&A) expense.

It is now February 2019 and the bicycle segment is considering purchasing helmets internally (from the helmet segment) to include it as part of a package with each bike. The bicycle segment is able to purchase the same type of helmets from an outside supplier for a cost of $19/unit.

Required

a) Provide a possible example of a cost that would be included in traceable fixed manufacturing overhead. Explain why it would be considered a traceable fixed cost.

_____

_____

_____

_____

b) Provide a possible example of a common fixed cost for Ronin Bike Company. Explain why it would be considered a common fixed cost.

_____

_____

_____

_____

c) Prepare a segmented contribution margin statement for January 2019.

	Total	Bicycle	Helmet
Ronin Bike Company **Segmented Contribution Margin Statement** **For the Month Ended January 31, 2019**			
		Segment (Product Line)	

d) Assume Ronin Bike Company uses negotiated transfer prices and the helmet segment is always operating at capacity. For the potential internal transfer of helmets from the helmet segment to the bicycle segment, what is the range of acceptable transfer prices, if any? Explain your reasoning.

e) Assume Ronin Bike Company uses cost-plus pricing for the internal transfers of goods. The transfer price of a helmet is determined by increasing cost by 50%.What is the difference in transfer price if absorption (full) cost is used as the cost base instead of variable cost?

Critical Thinking

CT-1

Gordon Sparks Ltd. sells ergonomic chairs. The company implemented a new bonus structure for all of their managers. If net income increased from the previous year, managers would be rewarded with 0.5% of the increase in net income.

In January of last year, Mingle Nicholson was hired as the manager of the marketing department. As the marketing manager, he was responsible for seeking external opportunities, managing budgets and understanding the current and potential customers. Every three or four days, Mingle would meet with the sales manager, Logan Freidman. The meeting was usually about past sales, and whether there were changes to the selling strategy. This information was extremely important to Mingle, since he was responsible to ensure the marketing objectives are aligned with the sales objectives.

During the year, Mingle made several changes to Gordon Sparks' marketing strategy. Mingle created a set of popular commercials, which were a complete success. Each commercial reached over 5,000,000 views on YouTube.

However, by the end of that year, Mingle realized that he did not receive a bonus from the company because the company's overall financial performance remained the same. Discuss the appropriateness of the company's bonus policy.

Chapter 10

CAPITAL BUDGETING

LEARNING OBJECTIVES

LO 1 Describe the concept of capital budgeting

LO 2 Evaluate investments using the non-discounted capital budgeting approach

LO 3 Evaluate investments using the discounted capital budgeting approach

LO 4 Rank different investments in order of preference

LO 5 Identify ethical issues related to capital budgeting

AMEENGAGE™ *Access ameengage.com for integrated resources including tutorials, practice exercises, the digital textbook and more.*

Assessment Questions

AS-1 LO 1

What is capital budgeting?

_____

_____

AS-2 LO 1

What is meant by the term "cost of capital"?

_____

_____

AS-3 LO 1

What are capital expenditures? Provide some examples of capital expenditures.

_____

_____

_____

AS-4 LO 1

What is an expansion decision?

_____

_____

_____

AS-5 LO 1

Identify the type of investment decision that involves deciding whether an old piece of equipment should be replaced by a new one.

_____

_____

AS-6 LO 1

Identify the investment decision that involves an organization deciding which equipment to purchase.

_____

_____

AS-7 LO 1

What is a cost-reduction decision?

_____

_____

_____

_____

AS-8 LO 1

What is a lease vs. buy decision?

_____

_____

_____

AS-9 LO 2 3

What are four examples of capital budgeting methods that help managers analyze whether a capital expenditure is worth pursuing?

_____

_____

_____

AS-10 LO 2

Explain the accounting rate of return method used in capital budgeting.

_____

_____

_____

AS-11 LO 2

What is a disadvantage of using the accounting rate of return method?

_____

_____

AS-12 LO 2

Explain the cash payback method in capital budgeting.

_____

_____

_____

AS-13 LO 2

What is a disadvantage of using the cash payback method?

_____

_____

AS-14 LO 2

In what circumstance can the formula method for the cash payback method be used?

_____

_____

AS-15 LO 3

What is the time value of money?

_____

_____

_____

AS-16 LO 3

Define compound interest.

_____

_____

AS-17 LO 3

What is future value?

_____

_____

AS-18 `LO 3`

Define present value.

_____

_____

AS-19 `LO 3`

What is an annuity?

_____

_____

AS-20 `LO 3`

How can an investor easily determine the initial investment required to receive a fixed payment each year in a given time period?

_____

_____

_____

AS-21 `LO 3 4`

Identify two capital budgeting methods that incorporate the time value of money into their analysis.

_____

_____

AS-22 `LO 3`

Describe the net present value (NPV) method.

_____

_____

_____

AS-23 `LO 3`

Explain the internal rate of return (IRR) method in capital budgeting.

_____

_____

AS-24 `LO 3`

What does the salvage value of an asset refer to?

_____

_____

_____

AS-25 LO 3

What is the difference between the NPV and the IRR method?

_____

_____

_____

_____

AS-26 LO 4

When comparing two proposals that both have positive NPVs, what must decision-makers rely on to make a more meaningful comparison and what does it do?

_____

_____

_____

_____

AS-27 LO 4

Describe the IRR decision rule.

_____

_____

_____

_____

AS-28 LO 5

A manager chooses Project A over another, equally acceptable project (Project B) because he has personally invested in the vendors involved with Project A. What IMA Ethical Standard has he violated and what are some repercussions that could occur?

_____

_____

_____

_____

_____

_____

_____

_____

_____

_____

_____

_____

Application Questions Group A

AP-1A LO 3

Suppose you are to receive $125 two years from now. Determine the present value of this amount if:

a)   The interest rate is 5%

_____

_____

_____

b)   The interest rate is 7%

_____

_____

_____

c)   The interest rate is 10%

_____

_____

_____

AP-2A LO 3

Assuming the interest rate is 12%, what is the present value of a $1,500 payment you will receive in:

a)   2 years?

_____

_____

_____

b)   5 years?

_____

_____

_____

c)   10 years?

_____

_____

_____

AP-3A LO 3

Use the information in the table to calculate the present value of the annuity.

Annual Payment	$40,000
Discount Rate	6%
Number of Years	10

AP-4A LO 3

Melissa Van has estimated that for the next 10 years her business will experience a net annual cash inflow of $60,000. Based solely on the cash flows for the next 10 years, how much is the business worth today? Assume an interest rate of 7%.

AP-5A LO 3

Your grandmother said she will give you $700 five years from now. How much is the $700 worth today if the discount rate is 5%?

AP-6A LO 3

Fill in the blanks for each of the following independent scenarios (A–D).

Scenario	A	B	C	D
Future Value (Single Payment)	$50,000	$10,000	$22,500	$9,000
Discount Rate	6%			14%
Number of Years		4	7	
Present Value Factor	0.5584	0.8227	0.4817	0.3506
Present Value		$8,227		$3,155.40

AP-7A LO 3

Fill in the blanks for each of the following independent scenarios (A–D).

Scenario	A	B	C	D
Annual Net Cash Flow	$15,000		$14,500	$10,000
Discount Rate	10%		7%	11%
Number of Payments		5		
Present Value of Annuity Factor	5.3349	3.9927	7.0236	
Present Value of Annuity		$159,708		$31,024

AP-8A LO 3

Fill in the blanks for each of the following independent scenarios (A–C).

Scenario	A	B	C
Required Initial Investment		$143,983.80	$159,144.72
Annual Net Cash Flow	$55,000	$20,500	
Number of Periods	4	10	
Internal Rate of Return			3%
Present Value of Annuity Factor	3.1024		9.2526

AP-9A LO 1 3

The following table indicates the net cash flows of a capital asset.

Year	Net Cash Flow
0	($10,000)
1	5,000
2	7,100

Assume the required rate of return is 10%. Determine the net present value of this asset.

_____

_____

_____

_____

_____

AP-10A LO 2

The following table indicates the net cash flows of a capital asset.

Year	Net Cash Flow
0	($220,000)
1	60,000
2	60,000
3	60,000
4	60,000

Calculate the cash payback period using the formula method.

_____

_____

_____

_____

_____

AP-11A LO 2

David is considering purchasing a new point-of-sale computer system for his store. The computer system will allow cashiers to process sales and returns quicker, plus it will easily integrate with his inventory management system. The new computer system will cost David $30,000 to purchase and setup.

Required

a) The expected net cash flow from savings is shown in the table below. Using the cash payback method, how long will it take for David to recover his investment?

Year	Expected Net Cash Flow	Cumulative Net Cash Flows
0	($30,000)	
1	5,000	
2	7,000	
3	9,000	
4	8,000	
5	6,000	

_____

b) If David has a policy of only accepting investments with a payback period of four years or less, should he invest in the point-of-sale computer system?

_____

_____

_____

AP-12A LO 2

Sarah is in charge of production at a factory that manufactures car bumpers. She has been presented with the option to buy a robotic machine that will assemble bumpers faster than her current machine, and will require less labor to operate it. The new machine will cost her $950,000 and is expected to last five years.

Required

a) The expected cash flow from savings is shown in the table below. Using the cash payback method, how long will it take Sarah to recover the cost of the initial investment?

Year	Expected Net Cash Flow	Cumulative Net Cash Flow
0	($950,000)	
1	225,000	
2	260,000	
3	280,000	
4	315,000	
5	310,000	

b) If Sarah has a policy that any investment should have a payback period of less than its useful life, should she invest in this machine?

AP-13A LO 2

Scarlett is the manager of a marketing department, and is considering a project that will cost $450,000 to implement. The project will last three years until it would be shut down. The incremental operating income is shown below.

Year	Incremental Operating Income
1	$65,000
2	45,000
3	40,000

Required

a) Calculate the ARR for the project.

b) If Scarlett's required rate of return is 12%, should she proceed with the project?

_____

_____

_____

AP-14A LO 2

Gene runs Gee Candy Inc. and is deciding whether to purchase an automated packaging machine. The old packaging machine Gee Candy currently uses is slow and requires a lot of maintenance to keep it running. The old machine can be sold for $5,000. The new automated packaging machine is fast and will require less maintenance. It will cost $425,000 to purchase and is expected to last four years. Gee Candy uses the accounting rate of return to make investment decisions. During the four years, the new machine is expected to produce the following incremental operating income.

Year	Incremental Operating Income
1	$80,000
2	75,000
3	60,000
4	55,000

Required

a) Calculate the ARR for the new machine.

_____

_____

_____

_____

b) If Gene's required rate of return is 13%, should he purchase the automated packaging machine?

_____

_____

_____

AP-15A LO 2

Fashion Boutique is considering purchasing a point-of-sale (POS) computer system for $40,000. Sales associates are currently performing various tasks, including providing customer service, selling products, determining sales patterns and identifying items for reorder. Since a POS system can help manage inventory, flag items for reorder and analyze sales patterns, this will reduce employee workload significantly. As a result, the owner believes the boutique will benefit from cash savings of $6,500 per year in labor costs.

Calculate the cash payback period of this investment.

_____

_____

_____

AP-16A LO 1 3

Two days ago, one of Morees Manufacturing Inc.'s major machines stopped working. In order to meet product demands, the company needs a new machine. The company is deciding to either lease or purchase a new machine. The company can lease the machine from LeaseIt Ltd. under a five-year contract. The lease cost would be $60,000 per year. On the other hand, Morees can purchase a machine from BuyIt Ltd. for $350,000. Assume Morees has a required rate of return of 10%.

Use the NPV method to determine which alternative the company should accept.

_____

_____

_____

_____

_____

_____

_____

_____

_____

AP-17A LO 1 3

The Coby Company would like to buy equipment to increase production capacity. The equipment costs $235,568 and has an estimated useful life of 10 years. The company believes that this investment will generate an additional net cash flow of $40,000 per year.

Required

a) Determine the internal rate of return of this investment.

_____

_____

_____

_____

_____

b) Assume the company has a required rate of return of 12%. Using the IRR method, should the company purchase the equipment?

_____

_____

_____

_____

AP-18A LO 1 3 4

Harold Coop is considering investing in either ABC or ZYX. Both investments ABC and ZYX cost $10,000. In order to make the purchase, Harold needs to obtain a loan from the bank at an interest rate of 7%. The bank is only willing to offer Harold $10,000. The following table outlines the expected net cash flows from each investment.

Year	ABC	ZYX
1	$500	$8,000
2	1,000	5,000
3	3,500	4,000
4	6,000	2,000
5	9,000	1,000
Total	$20,000	$20,000

Based on the NPV method, which investment should Harold purchase?

_____

_____

_____

_____

_____

_____

_____

_____

_____

_____

AP-19A LO 1 2 3

The Georgio Cranium Corporation is considering replacing the old binding equipment with a new one at a cost of $300,000. With the new equipment, the company expects to save $40,000 in maintenance costs per year, all cash savings. These savings in maintenance costs represent both an increase in cash flow and an increase in incremental operating income. The new binding equipment has an estimated useful life of 8 years with no salvage value. The company's required rate of return is 12%. The old binding equipment has no salvage value.

Required

a) Assume the company wants to recover their initial investment on the new equipment in eight years. Based on the payback method, should Georgio Cranium purchase the new equipment?

_____

_____

_____

_____

_____

b)   If the ARR method is used, should Georgio Cranium purchase the new equipment?

_____

_____

_____

_____

c)   If the NPV technique was used, should Georgio Cranium purchase the new equipment?

_____

_____

_____

AP-20A LO 1 3

Toby Gordano is starting school in September, and needs a car for the next six years. He is currently deciding to either purchase a used car for $25,000 or lease it from CheapLease Inc. If Toby decides to buy a car, he would incur the following costs per year:

Maintenance	$2,100
Insurance	1,800
Car Wash	800
Gas	900

On the other hand, Toby can lease the car under a six-year agreement at a lease cost of $8,700 per year. As part of the lease, CheapLease Inc. would provide all the required maintenance. Toby would still be responsible for the cost of car washes, gas and insurance.

Assume Toby has a required rate of return of 12%.

Required

a)   Using the NPV method, which alternative should Toby choose?

_____

_____

_____

_____

_____

_____

_____

_____

_____

_____

_____

_____

_____

_____
_____
_____
_____

b)   Determine the lease payment at which Toby would be indifferent to purchasing or leasing the car.

_____
_____
_____

AP-21A LO 1 2 3

Big Red Co. is interested in replacing its old machine. The machine the company is considering purchasing costs $96,700 with a useful life of ten years. By replacing the old machine with a new one, the company can reduce annual maintenance and repair costs by $7,900. In addition, the new machine can be sold for $20,000 at end of its useful life. If the company decides to accept this project, they can sell the old machine for $2,000.

Required

a)   Determine the payback period for the new machine.

_____
_____
_____
_____
_____

b)   Assume the company accepts projects if the payback period is less than the assets' useful life. Based on the payback method, should Big Red replace its old machine?

_____
_____
_____

c)   Now assume Big Red wants to use the NPV technique with a required rate of return of 10%. Determine whether the company should accept the project using the NPV method.

_____
_____
_____
_____

d)   Using the NPV technique, what is the maximum acceptable price to pay for this new machine?

_____

_____

_____

AP-22A LO 2

You are considering investing in an ice cream franchise called "The Ice Shack". The franchisees have two options. The first option involves operating a mobile ice cream truck. The second option involves opening a small store in a secondary plaza with space to sit up to 8 people. The cash flows for both options are shown below. Assume that the annual cash inflows for both options will occur for 10 years.

	Truck	Store
Initial Investment	$24,300	$50,300
Annual Cash Inflow	10,400	15,300

Based on the payback technique, which option should you invest in?

_____

_____

_____

_____

_____

_____

_____

_____

_____

_____

_____

_____

_____

_____

_____

_____

_____

_____

_____

AP-23A LO 1 3

The following table compares two capital assets, Model S800 and X780:

	Model S800	Model X780
Original Cost	$950,000	$1,100,000
Annual Variable Costs		
Direct Materials Usage	$650,000	$650,000
Direct Labor Usage	$1,100,000	$800,000
Annual Fixed Costs	$500,000	$600,000
Useful Life	7 years	7 years
Required Rate of Return	10%	10%
Salvage value (at the end of useful life)	$40,000	$80,000

OGY Corp. is currently using Model S800 to manufacture its products. A week ago, Mega Good Co. approached OGY regarding a new machine, Model X780. Mega Good has pointed out that while the X780 will still require the same amount of direct materials to manufacture the products, they promise that less operators will be needed to run the X780. The X780 is more automated than the S800. However, this increase in automation will require a higher annual maintenance cost. If OGY accepts this replacement project, OGY can immediately sell their S800 for $140,000. Using the NPV technique, should OGY replace its existing machine?

AP- 24A LO 2 3

Wonton Hut is considering purchasing a $12,926 machine to make wontons. The machine will decrease the annual direct labor costs by $5,000, but will increase annual fixed costs by $3,000. Assume the useful life of the asset is 8 years and that the required rate of return is 6%.

Required

a) Determine when Wonton Hut will recover its initial investment.

_____

_____

_____

_____

_____

b) Calculate the IRR of this investment. Should Wonton Hut purchase the machine?

_____

_____

_____

_____

_____

c) Should Wonton Hut purchase the machine if the NPV technique is used?

_____

_____

_____

AP-25A LO 2 3

Tippy Toe Spa Company offers various services, such as facials, laser hair removal and microdermabrasion. Currently, the company is considering purchasing the following spa equipment:

	Laser Hair Removal Machines	Microdermabrasion Machines	Facial Oxygen Units
Cost per Machine	$65,120	$30,850	$25,550
Annual Cash Inflow	125,500	213,750	39,625
Annual Cash Outflow	90,000	197,500	27,375
Required Rate of Return	12%	14%	6%
Useful Life	3 years	4 years	2 years
Salvage Value	900	840	0

Assume that each equipment's annual cash flow will occur for the period equal to its useful life.

Required

a) Determine which project(s), if any, should be invested in if the NPV method is used to evaluate these investments.

_____

_____

_____

_____

_____

_____

_____

_____

_____

_____

_____

_____

_____

_____

_____

_____

_____

_____

_____

_____

b) For each piece of equipment, determine the maximum acceptable price using the NPV method.

_____

_____

_____

_____

_____

_____

_____

_____

_____

c) Determine the payback period for each piece of equipment.

_____

_____

_____

_____

_____

_____

_____

_____

_____

_____

_____

_____

d) Assume the company accepts projects if the payback period is less than the asset's useful life. Using the payback method, should TippyToe invest in these assets?

_____

_____

_____

AP-26A LO 2 3

Blingalicious Ltd. is known for their customized jewellery. For the past decade, the company has been doing very well. The owner, Queenie Gold, is currently thinking of selling customized hair accessories. Queenie has provided the following information regarding the new product line.

Startup Costs	
Equipment	$70,000
Advertising	2,600
Annual Revenue	120,000
Annual Expenses	
Labor	50,000
Materials	40,000
Equipment Maintenance	10,000

Additional Information:

- All revenues and costs are dealt in cash.
- Queenie expects to consistently generate income for the next four years.
- Queenie requires a 9% rate of return for this particular product line.

Required

a)   Determine IRR for this investment. Should Queenie invest in the new project?

_____

_____

_____

_____

_____

_____

_____

_____

b)   Should Queenie invest in the new product, if the NPV method is used instead?

_____

_____

_____

c)   Describe one difference between the NPV and IRR method.

_____

_____

_____

d)   If Queenie decides to accept the project, how long will it take to recover her initial investment?

_____

_____

_____

Application Questions Group B

AP-1B LO 3

Suppose your grandmother is going to give you $500 for your birthday five years from now. Determine the present value of this amount if:

a)   The interest rate is 2%

b)   The interest rate is 6%

c)   The interest rate is 9%

AP-2B LO 3

Assuming the interest rate is 5%, what is the present value of a $750 payment you will receive in:

a)   1 year?

b)   3 years?

c)   7 years?

AP-3B LO 3

Use the information in the table to calculate the present value of the annuity.

Annual Payment ($)	15,000
Discount Rate (%)	12
Number of Years	15

_____

_____

_____

AP-4B LO 3

Because of an investment project, Heath Melvin has estimated that his business will experience an increase in net annual cash inflow of $45,000 for the next 10 years. Based solely on the cash flows, how much is the investment project worth today? Assume an interest rate of 4%.

_____

_____

_____

_____

AP-5B LO 3

You have loaned your brother a sum of money. If he will pay you back $1,000 in three years, how much did you loan him today if the discount rate is 7%?

_____

_____

_____

_____

_____

AP-6B LO 3

Fill in the blanks for each of the following independent scenarios (A–D).

Scenario	A	B	C	D
Future Value (single payment)		$17,000		$39,000
Discount Rate	4%	15%	7%	
Number of Years			7	20
Present Value Factor	0.7026	0.5718		0.1784
Present Value	$31,617		$76,280.75	

AP-7B LO 3

Fill in the blanks for each of the following independent scenarios (A–D).

Scenario	A	B	C	D
Annual Net Cash Flow	$2,000	$13,600		
Discount Rate	10%			11%
Number of Payments	10	7	15	
Present Value of Annuity Factor			9.1079	7.9633
Present Value of Annuity		$78,695.04	$12,751.06	$91,577.95

AP-8B LO 3

Fill in the blanks for each of the following independent scenarios (A–D).

Scenario	A	B	C
Required Initial Investment	$41,882.40	$161,056.00	$68,819.40
Annual Net Cash Flow	$13,500	$32,000	$6,000
Number of Periods	4	7	20
Internal Rate of Return			
Present Value of Annuity Factor	3.1024	5.033	11.4699

AP-9B LO 1 3

The following table indicates the net cash flows of a capital asset.

Year	Net Cash Flow
0	($25,000)
1	17,000
2	8,300

Required

a) Assume the required rate of return is 8%. Determine the net present value of this asset.

b) Should be company invest in this project? Why or why not?

AP-10B LO 2

The following table indicates the net cash flows of a capital asset.

Year	Net Cash Flow
0	($160,000)
1	45,000
2	45,000
3	45,000
4	45,000

Required

a) Calculate the cash payback period using the formula method.

_____

_____

_____

_____

b) Under what circumstances should this business undertake this investment?

_____

_____

AP-11B LO 2

Domino Ltd. is considering purchasing software for inventory control. The software will cost $17,500 to purchase and set up, and will have an ongoing service contract. The software company guarantees Domino Ltd. will have an easier time ordering and controlling its inventory levels, and reducing storage costs and losses due to theft or breakage.

Required

a) The expected net cash flow from savings is shown in the table. Using the cash payback method, how long will it take for Domino to recover its investment?

Year	Expected Net Cash Flow	Cumulative Net Cash Flows
0	($17,500)	
1	3,000	
2	7,000	
3	4,500	
4	5,000	
5	6,000	

_____

_____

b) If Domino has a policy of only accepting investments with a payback period of four years or less, should it invest in the new software and service?

_____

_____

AP-12B LO 2

Yeung's company produces vegetable peelers and other types of kitchen gadgets made using plastic casting. The company has been looking into new options to produce plastic handles for its gadgets and it has a couple of options. The one that management currently prefers produces cast plastic handles at nearly twice the current production output. This new machine must be ordered from Switzerland, costs $665,000 and is expected to last seven years.

Required

a) The expected cash flow from savings is shown in the table below. Using the cash payback method, how long will it take Yeung's company to recover the cost of the initial investment?

Year	Expected Net Cash Flow	Cumulative Net Cash Flows
0	($665,000)	
1	106,000	
2	97,000	
3	94,000	
4	92,000	
5	91,000	
6	83,000	
7	81,000	

_____

_____

b) If Yeung's company has a policy that any investment should have a payback period of less than its useful life, should it invest in the new machine?

_____

_____

AP-13B LO 2

Johansen Mack is the fundraising manager for a large charity. He is currently considering a new fundraising campaign that will cost the marketing department $175,000 to run over the next four years. The incremental operating income is shown in the table below.

Year	Incremental Operating Income
1	$55,000
2	30,000
3	15,000
4	5,000

Required

a) Calculate the accounting rate of return (ARR) for the project.

_____

_____

_____

_____

_____

b) If the charity needs to earn a minimum required rate of return of 10%, should it proceed with the project?

_____

_____

AP-14B LO 2

Chris Stanley owns More Clean, an industrial cleaning contractor that services major office buildings. Chris has been using an old wax polisher for the floors, but he's recently heard of a new type of floor polishing machine that is lighter and faster than his old one. If Chris decides to buy the new polisher, he can sell the old machine for $3,500. The new machine costs $27,000 and is expected to last five years with no residual value at the end of its useful life. Chris uses the accounting rate of return method to make investment decisions. During the five years, the new machine is expected to produce the following incremental operating income.

Year	Incremental Operating Income
1	$4,000
2	4,700
3	4,800
4	5,000
5	4,900

Required

a) Calculate the accounting rate of return (ARR) for the new machine.

_____

_____

_____

_____

_____

b) If Chris' required rate of return is 18%, should he purchase the new floor polishing machine?

_____

_____

_____

AP-15B LO 2

Ashley DaSilva is considering purchasing a new integrated accounting software system that can be customized for her car dealership. Including installation and customization, the new system will cost $75,000. Sales associates currently handle all aspects of the business, from selling new and used cars, to purchasing used cars, to booking service appointments and selling accessories. Each different activity is currently entered into a different software package that is uploaded into an off-the-shelf accounting software application. The system has been working reasonably well, but is prone to errors resulting in customer losses and mispricing accessories and services. The new integrated software can streamline processes, making task entry faster, more accurate and easier to track. Based on discussions with the software implementation consultants, Ashley believes the new system will save the dealership $14,000 per year.

Required

a)   Calculate the cash payback period of this investment.

_____
_____
_____
_____

b)   What criteria do you need to decide if this is a good investment for Ashley to make?

_____
_____
_____

AP-16B LO 1 3

Fixitall Manufacturing produces cable fasteners for home use. Demand for these products has skyrocketed recently and Fixitall must ramp up its manufacturing capacity. The current production equipment is at capacity so Fixitall needs a new machine and must decide whether to purchase or lease. Fixitall can either lease a machine for $78,000 per year for four years, or it could purchase the machine for $275,000. Assume that Fixitall has a required rate of return of 8%. Use the NPV method to determine what alternative the company should accept.

_____
_____
_____
_____
_____
_____
_____
_____
_____
_____
_____

AP-17B LO 1 3

RX Distillery would like to buy a new still to produce methyl alcohol for medical labs. The equipment costs $358,278 and has an estimated useful life of 8 years. RX believes that the new still will generate an additional net cash flow of $60,000 per year.

Required

a) Determine the internal rate of return (IRR) of this investment.

b) Assume the company has a required rate of return or 10%. Using the IRR method, should the company purchase the equipment?

AP-18B LO 1 3 4

Cooper Hastings is considering investing in Project Bingo or Project Bongo, each of which cost $15,000. To make the purchase, Cooper needs a bank loan, which he can get for an interest rate of 12% for up to the required $15,000. The following table outlines the expected net cash flows from each investment project.

Year	Project Bingo	Project Bongo
1	$2,500	$3,000
2	3,500	3,750
3	3,750	9,500
4	9,500	3,500
5	3,000	2,500
Total	$22,250	$22,250

Based on the NPV of each project, which one should Cooper invest in?

_____
_____
_____
_____
_____
_____
_____

AP-19B LO 1 2 3

Martin Martian Corp. produces direct ad mail and is considering a new machine that folds letter-sized address admail and inserts them into pre-addressed envelopes that would cost $370,000. Using this machine, Martin Martian Corp. can reduce its operating costs by $5,000 per month. These savings represent an increase in cash flow and an increase in incremental operating income. The new machine has an estimated useful life of 6 years with no salvage value. The company's required rate of return is 7% and its old machine has no salvage value.

Required

a) Assume the company wants to recover its initial investment in six years. Based on the payback method, should Martin Martian Corp. purchase the new equipment?

_____
_____
_____
_____
_____
_____

b) If the ARR method is used, should Martin Martian Corp. purchase the new equipment?

_____
_____
_____
_____
_____
_____

c) If the NPV method is used, should Martin Martian Corp purchase the new equipment?

_____
_____
_____
_____
_____

d) Which of the three methods provides the best answer? Why?

_____

_____

_____

_____

_____

AP-20B LO 1 3

Tomas runs a bakery and is looking for a new industrial oven. He is currently deciding to either purchase a new one $20,000 or lease it from Kitchen Supply Inc. If Tomas decides to buy the new oven, he would incur the following costs annually for the unit's five-year useful life:

Gas line installation (one time)	$2,100
Gas	15,000
Inspection and service	1,000

If Tomas leases the oven, a five-year lease agreement would include regular service and inspections as part of its annual lease payment of $5,700. Tomas would still be responsible for the cost of gas and a one-time installation fee for the gas line under the lease. Assume Tomas has a required rate of return of 6%.

Required

a) Using the NPV method, which alternative should Tomas choose?

_____

_____

_____

_____

_____

_____

_____

_____

_____

_____

_____

_____

_____

_____

_____

_____

b)   At what price must the lease payment be for Tomas to be indifferent to either purchasing or leasing the new oven?

_____

_____

_____

AP-21B LO 1 2 3

Canola Bean Co. requires a new harvester for its farming operations. The new harvester will cost $450,000 and have an eight year useful life. By replacing the old machine with a new one, Canola Bean can reduce annual maintenance and repair costs by $38,000. It can also sell the new machine for $200,000 at end of its useful life. If the company decides to accept this project, they can sell the old machine for $125,000.

Required

a)   Determine the cash payback period for the new machine.

_____

_____

_____

_____

_____

_____

_____

_____

_____

_____

b)   Assume the company accepts projects if the payback period is less than the assets' useful life. Based on the payback method, should Canola Bean replace its old machine?

_____

_____

c)   Now assume Canola Bean wants to use the NPV method with a required rate of return of 8%. Should Canola Bean accept the project based on the results of the NPV method?

_____

_____

_____

_____

_____

_____

_____

d) Using the NPV method, what is the maximum acceptable price to pay for this new machine?

_____

_____

AP-22B LO 2

Big Jobs Delivery is trying to decide between two options for new delivery trucks. The new truck would be used for the next five years. Truck A is slightly larger so uses more fuel, but can handle larger loads that earn more revenue. Truck B has better fuel economy but would be used for more trips, incurring higher insurance charges and increased wear and tear on the vehicle. The expected cash flows for the next five years are:

	Truck A	Truck B
Initial Investment	$65,000	$55,000
Annual Cash Inflow	22,000	19,500

Required

a) Based on the cash payback method, which option should Big Jobs invest in?

_____

_____

_____

_____

_____

_____

_____

_____

_____

_____

_____

b) What other considerations might Big Jobs want to consider when it decides on a new truck?

_____

_____

_____

_____

_____

_____

_____

_____

_____

_____

AP-23B LO 1 3

The following table compares industrial weaving machines.

	Weavamatic	Weavexx
Original Cost	$275,000	$312,500
Annual Variable Costs		
Direct Materials Usage	$1,345,000	$1,345,000
Direct Labor Usage	$185,000	$117,000
Annual Fixed Costs	$238,000	$214,000
Useful Life	5 years remaining	5 years
Required Rate of Return	12%	12%
Salvage Value (at the end of useful life)	$37,500	$41,250

Rosie Corp. has been producing its fabrics using a Weavamatic, but it is looking to invest in a new weaving machine to improve its outputs and reduce waste. After doing some research and receiving information from some of the top producers of industrial weavers, the Weavexx is under consideration to replace the Weavamatic. Both machines will use the same amount of direct materials to produce fabric, but the Weavexx requires fewer direct labor hours for set up, but regular servicing is required to keep the machine operating in peak condition.

The Weavamatic can be sold immediately for $86,000 if Rosie decides to buy the Weavexx. Using an NPV calculation, would you advise Rosie to keep the old machine or buy the new one?

_____

_____

_____

_____

_____

_____

_____

_____

_____

_____

_____

_____

_____

_____

_____

_____

_____

_____

_____

AP-24B LO 2 3

Remy Barker owns El Gato Corp., which produces raw pet food for dogs and cats. Remy is looking to replace his meat grinder with one that is more automated at a purchase price of $21,529. The machine will decrease the annual direct labor costs by $12,000, but will increase annual fixed costs by $5,500. The new meat grinder will have a useful life of 4 years. El Gato Corp. requires an annual rate of return of 7%.

Required

a) When will El Gato Corp. recover its initial investment?

b) Calculate the IRR of this investment. Should El Gato Corp. purchase the machine?

c) Should El Gato Corp. purchase the machine if the NPV method is used?

AP-25B LO 2 3

Bubbles has been producing luxury soaps for the past five years, but knows that it must keep evolving if it wants to stay relevant in the market. It is therefore looking to expand its product offerings to include cosmetics. Bubbles is looking at producing high-end face creams that use a special emulsifier in its production. It is also looking to produce a line of hair products that requires different equipment than what is usually used in production. Lastly, the company is considering a line of scented candles to round out its portfolio of products.

	Face Creams	Hair Products	Candles
Setup Costs	$75,400	$95,750	$42,600
Annual Cash Inflow	$214,120	$196,300	$134,250
Annual Cash Outflow	$183,000	$187,500	$127,375
Required Rate of Return	8%	4%	6%
Project Life	4 years	3 years	5 years
Salvage Value	$1,100	$1,300	$2,200

Required

a) Determine the cash payback period for each piece of equipment.

_____

_____

_____

_____

_____

_____

_____

_____

_____

_____

_____

_____

d) Assume the company accepts projects if the payback period is less than the asset's useful life. In which
    project should Bubbles invest?

_____

_____

AP-26B LO 2 3

Shoe Haven is a well-known designer and producer of dress shoes for men and women. Recently, Shoe
Haven's management has been looking into starting a line of casual footwear. Its project team has come up
with the following figures regarding the proposed new line.

Startup Costs	
Equipment	$163,000
Plant Reorganization	250,000
Advertising	82,600
Annual Revenue	408,000
Annual Expenses	
Labor	125,000
Advertising	17,000
Materials	78,000
Equipment Maintenance	6,000

Additional Information:

- All revenues and costs are dealt in cash. Overhead costs, such as depreciation, have been omitted
  for this question.
- Shoe Haven expects revenues and costs to remain stable for the foreseeable future.
- Shoe Haven requires a 6% rate of return for this particular product line, which it intends to review
  in three years.

Required

a) Determine the IRR for this investment. Should Shoe Haven invest in the new project?

b) Should Shoe Haven set up the new product line based on the project's NPV?

c) If Shoe Haven decides to accept the project, how long will it take to recover its intial investment? Comment on the result compared to IRR and NPV.

Critical Thinking

CT-1 LO 1 3 4

Hocus Pocus Company wants to increase sales by adding a new product line. The company is considering three different projects. However, its capital budget is limited to $1,500,000. In addition, the company requires a rate of return of 10%. The information concerning the three product lines is given below.

	Broomsticks	**Magic Wands**	**Crystal Balls**
Net Initial Investment	$1,170,000	$983,000	$2,210,000
Budgeted Income Statement for the next five years:			
Sales	$500,000	$450,000	$650,000
Cost of Goods Sold	80,000	50,000	32,000
Gross Margin	420,000	400,000	618,000
Marketing and Administrative Expenses	100,000	130,000	22,000
Net Income*	?	?	?

*Assume all amounts stated on the budgeted income statement are cash items.

Required

a) Determine the net present value for each project assuming all cash flows cease after five years.

_____

_____

_____

_____

_____

_____

_____

_____

_____

_____

_____

b) Which project should Hocus Pocus invest in and why?

_____

_____

_____

_____

_____

c)   If Hocus Pocus had a capital budget limit of $2,300,000, how should they invest it?

Notes

Chapter 11

RELEVANT COST AND DECISION-MAKING

LEARNING OBJECTIVES

LO 1 Distinguish between relevant and irrelevant costs

LO 2 Evaluate a variety of business decisions using relevant costs and differential analysis

LO 3 Identify ethical issues related to relevant costs and decision-making

AMEENGAGE™ *Access **ameengage.com** for integrated resources including tutorials, practice exercises, the digital textbook and more.*

Assessment Questions

AS-1 LO 1

What are relevant costs?

AS-2 LO 1

What are irrelevant costs?

AS-3 LO 1

What are sunk costs?

AS-4 LO 1

Provide two examples of sunk costs.

AS-5 LO 1

True or false: Sunk costs are sometimes relevant to a decision.

_____

_____

AS-6 LO 1

Define differential cost.

_____

_____

AS-7 LO 1

True or false: The opportunity cost of choosing one alternative is the total value of all other foregone alternatives.

_____

_____

AS-8 LO 1

Define opportunity cost.

_____

_____

AS-9 LO 1

Provide an example of a qualitative consideration when making a decision.

_____

_____

_____

AS-10 LO 1

Provide four common types of business decisions that are based on relevant cost principles.

_____

_____

_____

_____

AS-11 LO 2

In the keep or drop decision, which financial figure does the choice primarily depend on?

_____

_____

AS-12 LO 2

In the keep or drop decision, why is it beneficial to prepare a segmented contribution margin statement?

AS-13 LO 2

What is another term for the make or buy decision?

AS-14 LO 2

What is a special order?

AS-15 LO 2

Describe the product mix decision.

AS-16 LO 3

What are some ethical considerations concerning the decision-making process?

Application Questions Group A

AP-1A `LO` `1`

Jimmy currently owns a 2013 Toyota Corolla. He is considering replacing this car with a 2016 Corolla. The following is a list of some of the costs to consider:

2016 Corolla purchase price	$12,000
Parking at apartment (annually)	600
Insurance - old car (annually)	2,400
Advertising to sell old car	100
Gas consumption (annually)	6,000

Assume that the new Corolla will use the same engine as Jimmy's old Corolla (i.e. both cars will consume the same amount of gas). The cost for one parking spot at Jimmy's apartment is currently $600 per year. However, the landlord has notified Jimmy that the cost for one parking spot will soon increase to $800 per year. Jimmy's insurance agent mentioned that insurance will cost $3,600 per year for the new Corolla. The old Corolla can be sold for $9,000.

Determine costs and revenues that are relevant to Jimmy's decision. Explain your choices and state the specific amounts. Also explain the reason for omitting costs from the below table, if any.

	Relevant Costs	Relevant Revenues

_____

_____

_____

_____

AP-2A `LO` `1`

Wentworth Toys is a manufacturer of action figures for children. The primary machine used to manufacture the action figures is the model A15 machine. The company is considering replacing the old model A15 machine with a new model B20 machine. The change will have no effect on production costs, other than some savings in direct material costs due to less waste. If the model B20 machine is used, sales are expected to increase due to improved quality. The model A15 machine would be sold.

Check off the appropriate boxes to indicate whether each item is relevant or irrelevant.

	Relevant	Irrelevant
Sales revenue		
Direct materials		
Direct labor		
Variable manufacturing overhead		
Depreciation cost (to date) – model A15 machine		
Book value – model A15 machine		
Disposal value – model A15 machine		
Market value – model B20 machine (cost)		

AP-3A LO 1 2

Trifecta Sports Manufacturer produces equipment for three sports: baseball, basketball, and golf. The accountants prepared a segmented contribution margin statement for the past year based on the three types of products manufactured as shown below. The CEO is concerned with the basketball equipment segment as it has been showing a loss for the past few years.

Trifecta Sports Manufacturer Segmented Contribution Margin Statement For the Year Ended December 31, 2019				
	Baseball	**Basketball**	**Golf**	**Total**
Revenue	$500,000	$400,000	$200,000	$1,100,000
Less: Variable Costs	350,000	300,000	80,000	730,000
Contribution Margin	150,000	100,000	120,000	370,000
Less: Fixed Costs	90,000	150,000	35,000	275,000
Income from Operations	$60,000	($50,000)	$85,000	$95,000

Required

Recommend whether Trifecta should keep or drop the basketball equipment product line based on the following independent scenarios:

a) If the line is dropped, assume that all the fixed costs relating to the basketball equipment segment would remain with the company.

b) Assume that all the fixed costs relating to the basketball segment would no longer be incurred by the company if the product line is dropped.

c) Only 30% of the fixed costs relating to the basketball segment would remain with the company if the product line is dropped.

_____

_____

_____

_____

_____

_____

_____

_____

AP-4A LO 1 2

Pac Coast Airlines has been incurring losses for the past few years. In an attempt to improve the overall financial performance of the company, the general manager is considering discontinuing several of the flights. Flight 102 from Atlanta, Georgia to Paris, France is one such flight. The contribution margin statement for this particular flight is shown below.

Pac Coast Airlines Contribution Margin Statement For the Year Ended December 31, 2019	
	Flight 102
Revenue	$2,000,000
Less: Variable Costs	1,500,000
Contribution Margin	500,000
Less: Fixed Costs	800,000
Income from Operations	($300,000)

The following additional information is also available regarding flight 102:

- 80% of the segment's fixed costs will remain with the company if the flight is discontinued. The remaining 20% of the fixed costs will no longer be incurred by the company if the flight is discontinued.

- If the flight is discontinued, contribution margin will increase by a total of $200,000 in other segments of Pac Coast Airlines.

Should flight 102 be discontinued or retained?

_____

_____

_____

_____

_____

_____

_____

AP-5A LO 1 2

Turnington Company is currently manufacturing Part P119. It produces 50,000 units of Part P119 per year. This part is used in the manufacturing of many products produced by Turnington. The breakdown of the cost per unit for P119 is shown below.

Direct materials	$5.00
Direct labor	1.50
Variable overhead	3.00
Fixed overhead	4.00
Unit cost	**$13.50**

The fixed overhead cost (at $4/unit) would still remain with the company even if Turnington stops manufacturing Part P119. An outside supplier has offered to sell the same part to Turnington for $12. Currently, there is no alternative use for the capital assets used to produce Part P119. These capital assets will not be sold if the company chooses to buy Part P119.

Required

a) Should Turnington Company make or buy Part P119?

b) What is the maximum price Turnington should be willing to pay an outside supplier for the part?

c) If Turnington buys the part for $12 instead of making it, by how much will income from operations increase or decrease?

AP-6A LO 1 2

Jenson Monitors Ltd., a manufacturer of computer monitors, currently produces a 19-inch LCD monitor. The company's accounting department has reported the following annual costs of producing the LCD monitor internally:

Jenson Monitors Annual Production Costs for 19-inch LCD Monitor		
	Per Unit	**10,000 Units**
Direct materials	$25	$250,000
Direct labor	14	$140,000
Variable overhead	11	$110,000
Production supervisor's salary	7	$70,000
Depreciation of LCD manufacturing equipment	4	$40,000
Allocated fixed overhead	9	$90,000
Total cost	**$70**	**$700,000**

An external supplier has offered to provide Jenson Monitors 10,000 units of the same LCD monitor per year at a price of $45 each.

Also consider the following information:

- The LCD manufacturing equipment has no salvage value and has no other use aside from producing the 19-inch LCD monitors. It cannot be sold.

- The fixed overhead costs allocated to the LCD monitors are common to all items produced in the factory.

- The production supervisor will take over duties in another department if the monitors are purchased from the external supplier. If this is the case, his annual salary will drop to $65,000.

Should the company continue manufacturing the monitors internally or begin purchasing them from the external supplier?

Jenson Monitors Make or Buy Analysis					
	Production Cost Per Unit	**Per Unit Differential Costs**		**Total Differential Costs (10,000 Units)**	
		Make	**Buy**	**Make**	**Buy**

AP-7A LO 1 2

Hawk Rollers Company produces skateboards. Each skateboard has the following costs:

Direct materials	$8
Direct labor	6
Variable manufacturing overhead	7
Allocated fixed manufacturing overhead*	4
Unit cost	**$25**

*The fixed manufacturing overhead is common to the company.

The production capacity is 350,000 units per year. However, Hawk Rollers expects to produce only 250,000 units for the coming year. The company also has fixed selling costs of $600,000 per year and variable selling costs of $2 per unit sold. Each skateboard normally sells for $35 each.

Recently, a customer offered to buy 50,000 skateboards at special price of $24 each. This order would not have any variable selling costs because no sales commissions are involved.

Required

a) Based on a quantitative analysis, should the company accept the special order?

b) What qualitative factors may impact the above decision?

AP-8A LO 1 2

Zentech Phone Gear Inc. produces high quality, durable protective cases for a variety of cellular phones. The company just received a special order to produce 400 units of a modified case for a specific phone model. The unit cost for the regular case is $35 ($25 in total for variable costs and $10 for allocated fixed manufacturing overhead that is common to the company). A regular case is priced at $50/unit. Extra costs for the modified case would be as follows:

- Extra paint and plastic required for the modified case costs $2 per unit.
- Adjustments to the design of the modified case costs $2,000 (a one-time cost).

The price charged for a modified case is $55/unit. For each modified case produced and sold, the production and sale of a regular case must be given up. (i.e. Zentech is currently operating at full capacity).

Should the company accept the order for the modified cases?

AP-9A LO 1 2

A company offers two versions of its main product: basic and luxury. The manufacturing process for these products is capital-intensive (i.e. primarily relies on the use of machines). The unit contribution margins for basic and luxury are $30 and $45 respectively. The company has 300 uncommitted hours of machine time that can be allocated to manufacturing more products. The machine hours used to produce one unit of basic is 0.5. The machine hours used per unit of luxury is 1.

Required

a) Calculate the contribution margin per machine hour for each product.

b) Which product, basic or luxury, should be produced using the uncommitted machine hours? Assume that there are no capacity constraints.

c) How many units of the product selected in part b) will be produced using the uncommitted machine time?

_____

_____

_____

d) What is the company's increase in contribution margin if the product selected in part b) will be produced using the uncommitted machine time?

_____

_____

_____

AP-10A LO 1 2

Brunson Tables Ltd. manufactures three types of tables: wooden, plastic, and glass-surfaced. Data on price and costs for the units are shown below.

	Wooden	Plastic	Glass
Price	$90	$60	$110
Variable Cost	40	20	50
Allocated Fixed Cost	8	6	15
Profit per Unit	$42	$34	$45

The allocated fixed cost, which is fixed manufacturing overhead, is allocated to the three products using a rate of $2 per direct labor hour consumed by the product. There are 1,000 uncommitted hours of direct labor that can be allocated to manufacturing more products.

Required

a) Which one of the three products should be produced using the available direct labor hours? Assume that Brunson Tables will be within capacity to produce and sell the additional units.

	Wooden	Plastic	Glass

_____

_____

_____

_____

_____

_____

_____

_____

_____
_____
_____
_____

b)   What is the opportunity cost of producing glass tables using the available direct labor hours?

_____
_____
_____

Application Questions Group B

AP-1B LO 1

Juan currently owns a 2009 Honda Civic. To save money, he is considering replacing the 2009 Honda Civic with a 2012 Honda motorcycle. The following is a list of some of the costs to consider:

	Car	Motorcycle
2012 Honda motorcycle purchase price		$7,000
Monthly parking	$50	60
Annual insurance	1,440	2,160
Advertising to sell car	75	
Annual gas costs	7,500	3,500

If Juan buys a motorcycle, we wants secured underground parking, rather then the surface parking he currently has for his car. Juan expects the Honda Civic can be sold for $7,000. Determine costs and revenues that are relevant to Juan's decision. Explain your choices and state the specific amounts. Also explain the reason for omitting costs, if any.

	Relevant Costs	Relevant Revenues

AP-2B LO 1

Luxe Lotions produces locally-sourced, environmentally friendly skin care products. Business has been doing very well and Luxe is currently looking at replacing its bottling equipment with a more efficient model. The new machine will save electricity costs and reduce direct materials costs because it will reduce waste from spills. The new bottling machine will require the same number of direct labor hours to operate as the old machine. The new machine is expected to have no impact on sales. If the new bottling machine is purchased, the old machine would be sold.

Check the boxes to indicate whether each item is relevant or irrelevant. Explain what makes each relevant or irrelevant.

	Relevant	Irrelevant	Reason
Sales revenue			
Direct materials			
Direct labor			
Variable manufacturing overhead			
Depreciation cost (to date)—old bottling machine			
Book value—old bottling machine			
Disposal value—old bottling machine			
Market value—new bottling machine (cost)			

AP-3B LO 1 2

Triple Threat Toys produces dolls, action figures and building sets. The accountants prepared a segmented contribution income statement for the three types of products manufactured for the last year. The executive management team is concerned that the dolls segment has been showing a loss for the past few years.

Triple Threat Toys Segmented Contribution Income Statement For the Year Ended December 31, 2019				
	Action Figures	Dolls	Building Sets	Total
Revenue	$125,000	$200,000	$225,000	$550,000
Less: Variable Costs	76,000	165,000	165,000	406,000
Contribution Margin	49,000	35,000	60,000	144,000
Less: Fixed Costs	40,000	40,000	40,000	120,000
Income from Operations	$9,000	($5,000)	$20,000	$24,000

Required

Recommend whether Triple Threat should keep or drop the dolls equipment product line based on the following independent scenarios:

a) If the line is dropped, assume that all the fixed costs relating to the doll product segment would remain with the company.

_____

_____

_____

b) Assume that the company would no longer incur all the fixed costs relating to the doll product segment if it drops the product line.

_____

_____

c) Assume that 10% of fixed costs related to the doll product segment would remain with the company if the product line is dropped.

_____

_____

_____

_____

_____

_____

_____

AP-4B LO 1

Burrito Burro has been operating two take-out burrito restaurants and two food trucks in Miami for the past few years. Food preparation and storage for the restaurants and food trucks happens in the restaurants. In an attempt to improve the company's overall financial performance, Bob Burro, the owner, is considering whether he should close the restaurants. The contribution income statement for the restaurants is shown below.

Burrito Burro Contribution Income Statement For the Year Ended December 31, 2019	
	Restaurants
Revenue	$1,275,000
Less: Variable Costs	900,000
Contribution Margin	375,000
Less: Fixed Costs	400,000
Income from Operations	($25,000)

If the restaurants are closed, Burrito Burro will have to rent kitchen space to assist with food production and storage, so 60% of the segment's fixed costs would remain with the company. The remaining fixed costs would no longer be incurred if the restaurants are closed. Should the restaurants segment be discontinued or retained?

_____

_____

_____

AP-5B [LO 1]

Webbermart Company manufactures fasteners for use in machine production. It currently produces 100,000 units of Fastener 99 per year. This part is used in the manufacturing of many products produced by Webbermart. The breakdown of the cost per unit for Fastener 99 is shown below.

Direct Materials	$2.60
Direct Labor	0.80
Variable Overhead	0.65
Fixed Overhead	2.04
Unit Cost	**$6.09**

The fixed overhead cost (at $2.04/unit) would still remain with the company even if Webbermart stops manufacturing Fastener 99. An outside supplier has offered to sell the same part to Webbermart for $7.20. The machine Webbermart uses to produce Fastener 99 can only be used to make that part so it cannot be sold if the company decides to buy Fastener 99.

Required

a) Should Webbermart Company make or buy Fastener 99?

b) What is the maximum price Webbermart should be willing to pay an outside supplier for the part?

c) If Webbermart buys the part for the price offered by the supplier, by how much will operating income increase or decrease?

AP-6B LO 1

Cabinet Warehouse Ltd. manufacturers household cabinets, and currently makes a bathroom cabinet that can be customized. Jim, the company's production manager, asked the accounting department to compile a breakdown of costs for producing the customizable cabinet:

Cabinet Warehouse		
Annual Production Costs for Customizable Bathroom Cabinet		
	Per Unit	5,000 Units
Direct Materials	$8.30	$41,500
Direct Labor	5.00	25,000
Variable Overhead	2.65	13,250
Production Supervisor's Salary	13.50	67,500
Manufacturing Equipment Depreciation	2.00	10,000
Allocated Fixed Overhead	4.00	20,000
Total Costs	$35.45	$177,250

An external supplier has offered to provide Cabinet Warehouse 5,000 units of the same cabinet per year at a price of $25 each.

Additional information:

- The manufacturing equipment has no salvage value and cannot be used for any other purpose. It also cannot be sold as there is no market for the equipment.

- The fixed overhead costs allocated to the cabinets are common to all items produced in the factory.

If Cabinet Warehouse decides to purchase the cabinets instead of making them, the production supervisor will take over duties in another department with a different salary based on new responsibilities. The new salary would be $50,000. Should the company continue manufacturing the cabinets or purchase them from the external supplier?

	Cabinet Warehouse Make or Buy Analysis				
	Production Cost Per Unit	Per Unit Differential Costs		Total Differential Costs Per 5,000 units	
		Make	Buy	Make	Buy

AP-7B LO 1

Sticky Labels Printing Company produces specialty labels. Each specialty label sheet has the following costs:

Direct Materials	$1.02
Direct Labor	0.83
Variable Manufacturing Overhead	0.56
Allocated Fixed Manufacturing Overhead*	0.22
Unit Cost	**$2.63**

*The fixed manufacturing overhead is common to the company.

The production capacity is 500,000 sheets per year. However, Sticky Labels Printing expects to produce only 300,000 sheets for the coming year. The company's fixed selling costs are $55,000 per year and variable selling costs of $0.18 per unit sold related to commission. Each sheet of specialty labels normally sells for $5.00 each. Recently, a customer offered to buy 250,000 sheets of specialty labels at special price of $4 each. Because of how this order came in, it does not have any commission.

Required

a) Based on quantitative analysis, should the company accept the special order?

b) What qualitative factors may impact the above decision?

AP-8B LO 1 2

Starlight Manufacturing Inc. produces portable lighting that runs on a combination of solar and battery power. The lights are sold mostly through hardware stores and have become increasingly popular over the past two years. The company just received a special order to produce 1,250 units of a light with a titanium case to be used in a luxury car roadside emergency kit. The unit cost for the regular light is $45.50 ($34.00 in total for variable costs and $11.50 for allocated fixed manufacturing overhead that is common to the company). A regular light sells for $89.75/unit. Extra costs for the modified case would be as follows:

- Titanium and specialized paint required for the modified lights cost $15.65 per unit.
- Equipment modifications and design adjustments for the special order would be a one-time cost of $2,500.

The price charged for a modified case is $110.75/unit. Because Starlight Manufacturing was operating at capacity prior to receiving the special order, it will have to forego the contribution margin for a regular sale for each special order item produced and sold.

Should the company accept the order for the specialized lights?

AP-9B LO 1 2

A company offers two versions of its main product: regular and grand. The manufacturing process for these products is capital-intensive (i.e. primarily relies on the use of machines). The unit contribution margins for regular and grand are $40 and $85, respectively. The company has 200 uncommitted hours of machine time that can be allocated to manufacturing more products. The machine hours used to produce one unit of regular is 1. The machine hours used per unit of grand is 2.

Required

a) Calculate the contribution margin per machine hour for each product.

b) Which product, regular or grand, should be produced using the uncommitted machine hours? Assume that there are no capacity constraints.

_____

_____

c) How many units of the product selected in part b) above will be produced using the uncommitted machine time?

_____

_____

d) What is the company's increase in contribution margin if the product selected in part b) will be produced using the uncommitted machine time?

_____

_____

AP-10B LO 1 2

Coffee Machine Company Ltd. manufactures three models of it espresso machine: basic, deluxe, and luxury. The basic model is small, designed to fit on a kitchen counter and is designed for use in a small home. The deluxe model is similar to the basic model, but has a stronger pump and better-quality finishing and fittings. The luxury model can be used in a commercial coffee shop, has a strong pump and top-of-the-line finishings and fittings. Data on price and costs for the units are shown below.

	Basic	Deluxe	Luxury
Price	$200	$500	$1,500
Direct Materials	75	175	475
Direct Labor ($12 per hour)	60	180	360
Variable Manufacturing Overhead	17	23	32
Allocated Fixed Manufacturing Overhead	15	45	90
Variable Selling Costs	2	20	120
Profit per Unit	$31	$57	$423

Required

a) Calculate the contribution margin per direct labor hour to produce each model.

_____

_____

_____

_____

_____

_____

b) What is the opportunity cost of producing Luxury espresso machines using the available direct labor hours?

_____

_____

_____

_____

Critical Thinking

CT-1 LO 1 2

After spending two years and $10,000,000 on developing a new product, Beat It Company has found out that a competitor—Thriller Inc.—has also developed a similar product that directly competes with them. Since Thriller got its product to the market first, it has set the price the market is willing to pay. The price set is lower than Beat It's cost to build each unit, thus it can only sell its product at a loss. The company still has to spend $1,000,000 to advertise and market the product.

a) Should Beat It spend the money to advertise and market the product?

_____

_____

_____

_____

b) Suppose the price of Thriller's product on the market was high enough so Beat It could generate a profit, however not as great a profit as originally planned. Should Beat It spend the money to advertise and market the product? What considerations should be taken into account?

_____

_____

_____

_____

_____

_____

_____

_____

_____

_____

_____

_____

_____

_____

_____

_____

_____

_____

_____

Chapter 12

STRATEGY AND SUSTAINABILITY

LEARNING OBJECTIVES

LO 1   Define and explain the importance of strategic planning

LO 2   Understand the use of the balanced scorecard

LO 3   Understand the steps in creating a balanced scorecard

LO 4   Define and describe the concepts of corporate social responsibility and sustainability

LO 5   Define and describe the purpose of environmental management accounting

LO 6   Identify ethical issues related to strategy and sustainability

AMEENGAGE™ *Access **ameengage.com** for integrated resources including tutorials, practice exercises, the digital textbook and more.*

Assessment Questions

AS-1 LO 1

Define vision.

_____

_____

AS-2 LO 1

What is a mission statement?

_____

_____

_____

AS-3 LO 1

Define strategy.

_____

_____

AS-4 LO 1

What does the acronym SMART stand for in terms of setting objectives?

_____

_____

AS-5 `LO 1`

Provide two types of strategies.

_____

_____

AS-6 `LO 1`

What is a differentiation strategy?

_____

_____

AS-7 `LO 1`

Define cost leadership strategy.

_____

_____

AS-8 `LO 2`

What is a balanced scorecard?

_____

_____

AS-9 `LO 2`

Provide the four key perspectives involved in the balanced scorecard.

_____

_____

AS-10 `LO 2 3`

What is included in the financial perspective?

_____

_____

AS-11 `LO 2 3`

What is included in the customer perspective?

_____

_____

AS-12 `LO 2 3`

Explain the internal business process perspective on the balanced scorecard.

_____

_____

AS-13 LO 2 3

What is involved in the learning and growth perspective?

_____

_____

_____

_____

AS-14 LO 2

True or False: The four perspectives in the balanced scorecard are interdependent and ultimately impact the financial results of the business.

_____

_____

AS–15 LO 2

Define key performance indicators.

_____

_____

AS-16 LO 4

What is corporate social responsibility?

_____

_____

_____

AS-17 LO 4

If a company adopts a triple bottom line, what performance is being evaluated?

_____

_____

AP-18 LO 4

What are some benefits for a company that embraces corporate social responsibility?

_____

_____

_____

_____

_____

AS-19 LO 4

What can be included in a CSR report?

_____
_____
_____

AS-20 LO 5

What is environmental management accounting?

_____
_____

AS-21 LO 5

Under what circumstances would environmental management accounting be used?

_____
_____

AS-22 LO 5

What are some benefits of using environmental management accounting in a product- or process-related decision?

_____
_____
_____
_____
_____
_____
_____
_____

AS-23 LO 6

When setting performance targets, what could lead a manager to engage in unethical behavior?

_____
_____

AS-24 LO 6

Identify some situations that could lead managers to act in an unethical manner.

_____
_____
_____

Application Questions Group A

AP-1A LO 1

Caitlin has been working at ComfyWear Inc. for two months. Yesterday, her supervisor requested her to increase the company's profits by 5%. Determine whether the supervisor's request complies with the SMART principle.

_____

_____

_____

AP-2A LO 2

Indicate whether the following statements are true or false:

		True/False
a)	The success of a balanced scorecard relies only on upper management	
b)	The balanced scorecard is a strategic performance management framework that allows organizations to manage and measure the delivery of their strategy	
c)	SMART stands for significant, marketable, achievable, realistic and timely	

AP-3A LO 2 3

Cannon Jep is considering the following KPIs to use in his business:

KPIs
Return on equity
Earnings per share
Process error rates
Process delay time
Order-delivery time

Assume Cannon wants KPIs that *only* measure changes in stockholder's value. Should Cannon use all the above KPIs?

_____

_____

_____

_____

AP-4A LO 2

Kurt Major is interested in improving customer satisfaction. Which of the following should be used as key performance indicators?

a) Return on assets

b) Time taken to fulfill customer's requests

c) Debt to equity ratio

d) Number of customer complaints

e) Customer satisfaction ratings

AP-5A LO 2 3

HemmyHem Company provides clothing alteration services. Currently, the company is suffering a decrease in profits. Consider the following balanced scorecard and provide a possible solution regarding their unfavorable financial performance.

		Target Performance For June	Actual Performance For June
Financial Perspective			
Increase Profits	Net profit margin	10%	2%
	Return on equity	10%	3%
Customer Perspective			
Retain Customers	Retention rate	75%	60%
	Number of complaints received per month	11	20
Internal Processes Perspective			
Increase Efficiency	Average stitching time per project	20 minutes	20 minutes
Learning and Growth Perspective			
Employee Satisfaction	Employee turnover	3	2
	Employee Satisfaction Rating	7	8

AP-6A LO 2 3

Reorganize the following the table to ensure the perspectives, objectives and KPIs are aligned.

Perspective	Objectives	KPI
Customer	• Increase profitability	• Return on sales
Learning and Growth	• Increase the number of customers	• Number of new customers
Internal Processes	• Reduce delivery time	• Employee retention rate
Financial	• Increase employee satisfaction	• Order-delivery time

Perspective	Objectives	KPI

AP-7A LO 2 3

A	B	C
Perspective	**Objectives**	**KPI**
Financial	• Increase customer satisfaction	• Earnings per share
Customer	• Reduce bottlenecks	• Customer-satisfaction ratings
Internal Processes	• Improve quality of products	• Number of employee development programs
Learning and Growth	• Increase stockholder value	• Average process waiting time
	• Enhance employee skills	• Quality index
		• Percentage of customers retained

Required

a) For each perspective in column A, select the appropriate objectives from column B. Note that more than one objective can be used for each perspective.

A	B
Perspective	**Objectives**
Financial	
Customer	
Internal Processes	
Learning and Growth	

b) For each objective, select the appropriate KPIs from column C. Note that more than one KPI can be applied for each objective.

B Objectives	C KPI
• Increase stockholder value	
• Increase customer satisfaction	
• Reduce bottlenecks	
• Improve quality of products	
• Enhance employee skills	

AP-8A LO 1 2 3

Josie Mosie is the owner of a manufacturing company called PowerUp. PowerUp sells lithium ion batteries. The company's competitive strategy is to offer high quality lithium ion batteries with unlimited battery life. Josie created a balanced scorecard for PowerUp. This is the first time a balanced scorecard has been developed for the company.

Objectives	KPI
Financial Perspective	
• Net income margin	• Return on owner's equity
	• Increase owner's return
Customer Perspective	
• Acquire new customers	• Number of new customers
• Percentage of customers retained	
Internal Processes Perspective	
• Quality control	• Improve manufacturing capability
• Defect rates	• Retain customers
Learning and Growth Perspective	
• Align organization and employee goals	• Percentage of processes with advanced controls
• Employee satisfaction rating	

Required

a) Determine if PowerUp's strategy is based on cost leadership or differentiation.

_____

_____

_____

_____

_____

_____

_____

b) You have been recently hired as a consultant for PowerUp. Identify any problems with its current balanced scorecard.

_____

_____

_____

_____

_____

_____

_____

_____

_____

_____

_____

_____

_____

_____

_____

_____

c) Update Josie's balanced scorecard with the errors you identified in part b). Ignore target and actual performance.

Objectives	KPI

Application Questions Group B

AP-1B LO 1

You have been working for a small grassroots charity as the accountant. A recent reduction in funding means that you have to reduce the amount the charity will spend in the upcoming years. When you talk to the Executive Director about how to manage the reduced funding, what kind of goals will you recommend? Give an example of what a goal might look like.

_____

_____

_____

_____

_____

_____

_____

AP-2B LO 1 2

Indicate whether the following statements are true or false:

Statement	True or False
The success of a balanced scorecard relies only lagging indicators only.	
The balanced scorecard can help employees understand how their role contributes to the organization's success	
The balanced scorecard measures performance based on three perspectives: financial, customer, operational efficiency	

AP-3B LO 2 3

Pablo Gomez is considering the following KPIs to use in his business:

- Inventory levels
- Number of professional development hours
- Process error rates
- Percentage of customers returning
- Number of processes per function.

Pablo wants to focus on improvements to his company's internal process. Which of the KPIs listed should Pablo use?

_____

_____

AP-4B LO 2 3

Higher Learning College is interested in improving its employee engagement survey results. Which of the following should be used as key performance indicators?
- Accounts receivable turnover
- Employee turnover
- Return on investment
- Employee satisfaction ratings
- Number of professional development hours

AP-5B LO 2 3

Man Bun Brewing Company is a boutique brewery that produces a range of alcoholic beer products and distributes them at farmers' markets. Currently, the company is suffering a decrease in profits. Consider the following balanced scorecard and provide a possible solution regarding the company's unfavorable financial performance.

		Target Performance For October	Actual Performance For October
Financial Perspective			
Increase Profits	Net profit margin	12%	3%
	Return on investment	7%	2%
Customer Perspective			
Retain Customers	Retention rate	80%	78%
	Number of complaints received per month	6	7
Internal Processes Perspective			
Increase Efficiency	Number of spoiled batches	1	2
Learning and Growth Perspective			
Employee Satisfaction	Employee turnover	0	2
	Employee Satisfaction Rating	9	6

AP-6B LO 2 3

Reorganize the following the table to ensure the perspectives, objectives and KPIs are aligned.

Perspective	Objectives	KPI
Customer	Reduce error rates	Price Earnings Ratio
Learning and Growth	Increase stockholder value	Percentage of sales resulting in returns
Internal Processes	Reduce employee turnover	Number of returns
Financial	Reduce returns	Employee attrition rate

Perspective	Objectives	KPI

AP-7B LO 2 3

A	B	C
Perspective	**Objectives**	**KPI**
Financial	Decrease production costs	Gross profit margin
Customer	Grow revenue	Sales growth by period
Internal Processes	Improve customer retention	Time between new product introduction and going to market
Learning and Growth	Improve product quality	Defect rates
	Improve time to market	Percentage of return customers
	Increase manufacturing efficiency	Time to produce

Required

a) For each perspective in column A, select the appropriate objectives from column B. Note that more than one objective can be used for each perspective.

A	B
Perspective	**Objectives**

b) For each objective, select the appropriate KPIs from column C. Note that more than one KPI can be applied for each objective.

B	C
Objectives	**KPI**

AP-8B LO 1 2 3

Chuck Waylon is the owner of a manufacturing company called Bricks and Mortar. Bricks and Mortar sells composite building materials. The company's competitive strategy is to offer reasonably-priced quality composite building materials that are made using environmentally-sensitive production processes. Similar products sell for higher prices. Chuck created a balanced scorecard for Bricks and Mortar for the first time.

	Objectives	KPI
Financial Perspective		
	Cash flow	Cash received
	Increase gross margin	Gross margin
Customer Perspective		
	Improve time to market	Time to get a new product to market
	Customer returns	Improve customer satisfaction
Internal Processes Perspective		
	Improve employee performance	Reduce order errors
	Reduce reorder time	Time taken to place an order
Learning and Growth Perspective		
	Improve employee retention	Number of employees with long service
	Empower workforce	Number of line managers

Required

a) Is Bricks and Mortar following a cost-leadership or differentiation strategy? Support your answer.

_____

_____

_____

b) You have been recently hired as a consultant for Bricks and Mortar. Identify any problems with its current balanced scorecard.

_____

_____

_____

_____

_____

_____

_____

_____

_____

_____

_____

_____

c) Update Chuck's balanced scorecard and identify both the errors you identified in part b) and suggest a correction. Ignore target and actual performance.

	Objectives		KPI	
	Incorrect	**Correct**	**Incorrect**	**Correct**
Financial Perspective				
Customer Perspective				
Internal Processes Perspective				
Learning and Growth Perspective				

Critical Thinking

CT-1 LO 2

Freedmen Gort Company manufactures auto parts. In just one year, Freedmen went from a net profit of $20,000 to $35,000. The company provides the following balanced scorecard:

		Target Performance for 2019	Actual Performance for 2019
Financial Perspective			
Increase profits	Gross profit margin	20%	35%
	Return on equity	15%	16%
Customer Perspective			
Customer satisfaction	Retention rate	75%	85%
Market share	Market share of total	8%	10%
Internal Processes Perspective			
Improve product quality	Defect rate	4	2
Improve processes	Number of major improvements in manufacturing processes	4	4
Learning and Growth Perspective			
Employee empowerment	Percentage of employee suggestions implemented	25%	30%
	Employee satisfaction rating	7	9

Using the information on their balanced scorecard, explain how its financial performance improved in the past year.

_____

_____

_____

_____

_____

_____

_____

_____

_____

_____

_____

_____

_____

_____

Notes

Chapter 13

THE STATEMENT OF CASH FLOWS

LEARNING OBJECTIVES

LO **1** Classify operating, investing and financing activities

LO **2** Prepare a statement of cash flows using the indirect method

LO **3** Calculate book value and cash received for selling noncurrent assets

LO **4** Explain the concept of free cash flow and its importance for potential investors

LO **5** Discuss ethical issues related to cash flow

Appendix

LO **6** Prepare a statement of cash flows using the direct method

LO **7** Prepare a statement of cash flows in a spreadsheet using the indirect method

AMEENGAGE *Access **ameengage.com** for integrated resources including tutorials, practice exercises, the digital textbook and more.*

Assessment Questions

AS-1 LO 1

Is the statement of cash flows an optional statement? Explain.

AS-2 LO 1

Identify the three ways a business can generate and use cash.

AS-3 LO 1

What does cash flow from operating activities represent?

AS-4 LO 1

What does cash flow from investing activities represent?

AS-5 LO 1

What does cash flow from financing activities represent?

_____

_____

_____

AS-6 LO 2

Which financial statements are required to prepare a statement of cash flows?

_____

_____

AS-7 LO 2

Which items appear in the cash flow from operating activities section of the statement of cash flows using the indirect method?

_____

_____

_____

AS-8 LO 2

Which items appear in the cash flow from investing activities section of the statement of cash flows?

_____

_____

AS-9 LO 2

Which items appear in the cash flow from financing activities section of the statement of cash flows?

_____

_____

AS-10 LO 3

What does a gain on the sale of equipment indicate?

_____

_____

AS-11 LO 3

How is a gain on sale of equipment shown on the statement of cash flows using the indirect method?

_____

_____

_____

_____

AS-12 LO 4

Define free cash flow.

_____

_____

AS-13 LO 4

Why would an investor or creditor want to see a company show a positive free cash flow amount?

_____

_____

AS-14 LO 5

What are some actions a company may be tempted to take to unethically and artificially improve its statement of cash flows presentation?

_____

_____

AS-15 LO 6

What is the difference in the presentation of the statement of cash flows between the indirect and the direct methods?

_____

_____

_____

AS-16 LO 6

Using the direct method, how can we calculate the amount of cash spent on inventory?

_____

_____

_____

_____

AS-17 LO 7

When a statement of cash flows is prepared using a work sheet (spreadsheet), how is net income entered into the work sheet?

_____

_____

_____

———————   **Application Questions Group A**   ———————

AP-1A LO **1**

For each item listed, indicate how the item will impact cash flow (increase, decrease or no change) using the indirect method.

Item	Effect on Cash
Net Income	
Increase in Accounts Payable	
Decrease in Accounts Receivable	
Purchase of Property, Plant and Equipment	
Payment of Notes Payable	
Increase in Merchandise Inventory	
Pay Dividends	
Increase in Loans	
Increase in Prepaid Insurance	
Gain on Redemption of Bonds	
Issue Stock in Excess of Par Value	

AP-2A LO **2**

Indicate the section of the statement of cash flows where each item would be located (operating, investing or financing activities) using the indirect method.

Item	Section
Change in Accounts Payable	
Change in Merchandise Inventory	
Change in Property, Plant and Equipment	
Change in Long-Term Portion of Notes Payable	
Change in Current Portion of Notes Payable	
Change in Prepaid Rent	
Change in Accounts Receivable	
Change in Common Stock	
Gain on Sale of Property, Plant and Equipment	
Change in Paid-In Capital in Excess of Par Value	

AP-3A [LO 2]

The net income for the year ended on December 31, 2019 for RC Corporation was $120,000. Additional data for the year is provided below.

Loss on retirement of debt	$20,000
Purchase of property, plant and equipment	280,000
Depreciation of property, plant and equipment	14,000
Dividends declared	50,000
Decrease in accounts receivable	29,000
Loss on sale of equipment	13,000
Issue of common stock in excess of par value	10,000

Calculate the net cash provided (used) by operating activities using the indirect method.

_____

_____

_____

_____

_____

_____

AP-4A [LO 2]

Ashe Inc. reported the following data for 2019.

Income Statement	
Net Income	$30,000
Depreciation Expense	4,000
Balance Sheet	
Increase in Accounts Receivable	$9,000
Decrease in Accounts Payable	7,000

Calculate the net cash provided (used) by operating activities.

_____

_____

_____

_____

_____

_____

AP-5A LO 2

The net income for the year ended on August 31, 2019 for Wonderstruck Corporation was $147,000. Additional data for the year is provided below.

Purchase of property, plant and equipment	$257,000
Depreciation of equipment	$11,000
Dividends paid	$42,000
Net increase in accounts receivable	$22,000
Loss on sale of property	$17,000
Gain on retirement of debt	$10,000

Calculate the net cash provided (used) by operating activities.

_____

_____

_____

_____

_____

AP-6A LO 2

Mellon Incorporated had a net income for 2019 of $320,000. Included on the income statement was a loss on sale of equipment for $5,000, a gain on sale of investments for $15,000, depreciation of $8,000, loss on retirement of debt of $10,000 and interest of $3,000. Calculate the net cash provided (used) by operating activities using the indirect method. Assume that the balances of current assets (except cash) and current liabilities remain the same as last year.

_____

_____

_____

_____

_____

Analysis

Does net income, after being adjusted by the noncash items on the income statement, represent the actual amount of cash received through operating activities by the company during the year?

_____

_____

_____

AP-7A `LO 2`

The following information pertains to Tree Company for the fiscal year 2019.

Purchase of plant and equipment	$35,000
Purchase of long-term investments	$19,000
Increase in accounts receivable	$7,100
Repayment of bonds payable	$12,000
Depreciation of plant and equipment	$10,000

Calculate the net cash provided (used) by investing activities.

_____

_____

_____

AP-8A `LO 2`

The Marking Company's cash account decreased by $20,000. Net cash provided by operating activities was $17,000. Net cash used by investing activities was $22,000. Calculate the net cash provided (used) by financing activities.

_____

_____

_____

_____

_____

_____

_____

_____

_____

_____

AP-9A `LO 2`

The Grading Company's cash account decreased by $14,000. Net cash provided by operating activities was $21,000. Net cash used by investing activities was $22,000. Based on this information, calculate the net cash provided (used) by financing activities.

_____

_____

_____

_____

_____

AP-10A LO 3

Allen Woods has just started working as an accountant for Stickla Supplies. Unfortunately, the company had no proper accounting system in place and Allen had to start everything from scratch. He has been provided with some items from the company's balance sheet and income statement for the end of 2019.

Going through the company's purchase receipts and some other financial documents, Allen realized that Stickla purchased $2,500 worth of equipment in 2019. At the end of 2018, the balance of property, plant and equipment was $11,000 and the balance of accumulated depreciation was $2,900. Accounts payable . balance was not affected by any investment activities during 2019.

Accounts	2019
Property, Plant and Equipment	$10,000
Accumulated Depreciation	$3,600
Accounts Payable	$4,000
Notes Payable, Current Portion	$15,000
Retained Earnings	$5,400
Depreciation Expense	$1,200
Loss on Sale of Equipment	$300

Based on the information provided, help Allen fill the missing information in the table below.

Which section of the statement of cash flows is affected?	
How much PPE (book value before deducting accumulated depreciation) was sold in 2019?	
What was the accumulated depreciation for the PPE sold?	
What was the net book value of the PPE sold?	
How much cash was received from the sale?	
How much cash was paid out for the purchase?	
What was the net change in cash resulting from PPE?	

AP-11A LO 2

Balance sheet accounts for Planet Inc. contain the following amounts at the end of 2018 and 2019.

Planet Inc. Balance Sheet As at December 31	2019	2018
Assets		
Current Assets		
Cash	$7,500	$5,000
Accounts Receivable	21,000	15,000
Prepaid Expenses	2,500	2,000
Merchandise Inventory	37,000	28,000
Total Current Assets	68,000	50,000
Noncurrent Assets		
Equipment	196,000	175,000
Accumulated Depreciation	(41,000)	(32,000)
Total Noncurrent Assets	155,000	143,000
Total Assets	$223,000	$193,000
Liabilities		
Current Liabilities	$33,000	$33,000
Long-Term Liabilities	30,000	35,000
Total Liabilities	63,000	68,000
Stockholders' Equity		
Paid-In Capital		
Preferred Stock	50,000	45,000
Common Stock	20,000	15,000
Additional Paid-In Capital	5,000	0
Total Paid-In Capital	75,000	60,000
Retained Earnings	85,000	65,000
Total Stockholders' Equity	160,000	125,000
Total Liabilities and Stockholders' Equity	$223,000	$193,000

Assume current liabilities include only items from operations (e.g. accounts payable, taxes payable). Long-term liabilities include items from financing (e.g. bonds and other long-term liabilities).

Note that the company did not sell any equipment and did not borrow any additional long-term liabilities throughout the year.

Prepare the statement of cash flows for 2019 using the indirect method. Assume no dividends were declared or paid in 2019.

AP-12A LO 2 6

Breakwater Boats sells boating accessories. At the end of 2019, the income statement and comparative balance sheet were prepared as shown below.

Breakwater Boats Balance Sheet As at December 31		
	2019	**2018**
Assets		
Current Assets		
Cash	$73,870	$62,500
Accounts Receivable	94,800	87,500
Merchandise Inventory	327,000	245,700
Prepaid Expenses	14,500	14,500
Total Current Assets	510,170	410,200
Noncurrent Assets[1]		
Land	0	44,000
Equipment	340,000	340,000
Accumulated Depreciation	(26,200)	(24,500)
Total Noncurrent Assets	313,800	359,500
Total Assets	$823,970	$769,700
Liabilities		
Current Liabilities		
Accounts Payable	$52,600	$45,700
Notes Payable, Current Portion	8,500	8,500
Total Current Liabilities	61,100	54,200
Notes Payable, Long-Term Portion	50,100	58,600
Total Liabilities	111,200	112,800
Stockholders' Equity		
Common Stock	150,000	150,000
Retained Earnings	562,770	506,900
Total Stockholders' Equity	712,770	656,900
Total Liabilities and Stockholders' Equity	$823,970	$769,700

[1] During 2019, land was sold for a gain of $6,000. There was no purchase of equipment throughout the year.

Breakwater Boats	
Income Statement	
For the Year Ended December 31, 2019	
Sales	$562,000
Cost of Goods Sold	365,300
Gross Profit	196,700
Operating Expenses	
Depreciation Expense	1,700
Other Operating Expenses	61,200
Total Operating Expenses	62,900
Income from Operations	133,800
Other Income and Expenses	
Gain on Sale of Land	6,000
Income before Income Tax Expense	139,800
Income Tax Expense	48,930
Net Income	$90,870

Required

a) Prepare the statement of cash flows using the indirect method.

b) Prepare the statement of cash flows using the direct method. Assume accounts payable is only for the purchase of merchandise inventory. Do not show the reconciliation schedule of net income with net cash provided (used) by operating activities at the bottom of the statement of cash flows.

Analysis

Explain the main activities that caused Breakwater Boats' net cash flow to increase or decrease.

AP-13A LO 2 3 6

The balance sheet and income statement for Zooyo Appliance are presented below.

Zooyo Appliance Balance Sheet As at December 31		
	2019	**2018**
Assets		
Cash	$37,580	$15,000
Accounts Receivable	17,000	16,000
Merchandise Inventory	21,000	27,000
Total Current Assets	75,580	58,000
Land	110,000	80,000
Equipment	130,000	160,000
Accumulated Depreciation	(26,500)	(30,000)
Total Assets	$289,080	$268,000
Liabilities		
Current Liabilities		
Accounts Payable	$29,000	$35,000
Taxes Payable	18,000	18,000
Total Current Liabilities	47,000	53,000
Bonds Payable	80,000	65,000
Total Liabilities	127,000	118,000
Stockholders' Equity		
Common Stock	75,000	70,000
Retained Earnings	87,080	80,000
Total Stockholders' Equity	162,080	150,000
Total Liabilities and Stockholders' Equity	$289,080	$268,000

Zooyo Appliance Income Statement For the Year Ended December 31, 2019	
Sales	$142,000
Cost of Goods Sold	92,000
Gross Profit	50,000
Operating Expenses	
Depreciation Expense	4,500
Other Operating Expenses	13,550
Total Operating Expenses	18,050
Income from Operations	31,950
Other Income and Expenses	
Interest Expense	(4,350)
Loss on Sale of Equipment	(3,200)
Income before Income Tax Expense	24,400
Income Tax Expense	7,320
Net Income (Loss)	$17,080

Notes: There was no sale of land or purchase of equipment during the year. The company did not repay any bonds principal during the year. The company declared and paid dividends during the year.

Required

a)   Prepare the statement of cash flows for December 31, 2019 using the indirect method.

b) Prepare the statement of cash flows using the direct method. Assume accounts payable is only for the purchase of merchandise inventory. Do not show the reconciliation schedule of net income with net cash provided (used) by operating activities at the bottom of the statement of cash flows.

AP-14A LO 2 3 6

The balance sheet and income statement for Demgo Inc. are presented below.

Demgo Inc. Balance Sheet As at December 31	2019	2018
Assets		
Cash	$20,140	$21,000
Accounts Receivable	17,000	19,000
Merchandise Inventory	21,000	15,000
Total Current Assets	58,140	55,000
Land	110,000	60,000
Machinery	100,000	140,000
Accumulated Depreciation	(40,500)	(60,000)
Total Assets	$227,640	$195,000
Liabilities		
Current Liabilities		
Accounts Payable	$29,000	$25,000
Taxes Payable	22,000	22,000
Total Current Liabilities	51,000	47,000
Bonds Payable	70,000	65,000
Total Liabilities	121,000	112,000
Stockholders' Equity		
Common Stock	85,000	70,000
Retained Earnings	21,640	13,000
Total Stockholders' Equity	106,640	83,000
Total Liabilities and Stockholders' Equity	$227,640	$195,000

Demgo Inc. Income Statement For the Year Ended December 31, 2019	
Sales	$130,000
Cost of Goods Sold	72,000
Gross Profit	58,000
Operating Expenses	
Depreciation Expense	20,500
Other Operating Expenses	9,950
Total Operating Expenses	30,450
Income from Operations	27,550
Other Income and Expenses	
Interest Expense	(4,050)
Gain on Sale of Machinery	1,700
Income before Income Tax Expense	25,200
Income Tax Expense	7,560
Net Income (Loss)	$17,640

Notes: There was no sale of land.
Machinery was purchased for an amount of $80,000.
The company did not repay any bonds principal during the year.
The company declared and paid dividends during the year.

Required

a) Prepare the statement of cash flows for December 31, 2019 using the indirect method.

b)   Prepare the statement of cash flows using the direct method. Assume accounts payable is only for the
     purchase of merchandise inventory. Do not show the reconciliation schedule of net income with net cash
     provided (used) by operating activities at the bottom of the statement of cash flows.

AP-15A LO 2 3 6

The balance sheet and income statement for Vispara Company are presented below.

Vispara Company Balance Sheet As at December 31		
	2019	**2018**
Assets		
Cash	$133,400	$75,000
Accounts Receivable	47,000	26,000
Merchandise Inventory	72,000	42,000
Total Current Assets	252,400	143,000
Land	90,000	100,000
Equipment	90,000	130,000
Accumulated Depreciation	(45,000)	(60,000)
Total Assets	$387,400	$313,000
Liabilities		
Current Liabilities		
Accounts Payable	$35,000	$65,000
Taxes Payable	40,000	40,000
Total Current Liabilities	75,000	105,000
Bonds Payable	140,000	95,000
Total Liabilities	215,000	200,000
Stockholders' Equity		
Common Stock	85,000	75,000
Retained Earnings	87,400	38,000
Total Stockholders' Equity	172,400	113,000
Total Liabilities and Stockholders' Equity	$387,400	$313,000

Vispara Company Income Statement For the Year Ended December 31, 2019	
Sales	$380,000
Cost of Goods Sold	247,000
Gross Profit	133,000
Operating Expenses	
Depreciation Expense	5,000
Other Operating Expenses	22,550
Total Operating Expenses	27,550
Income from Operations	105,450
Other Income and Expenses	
Interest Expense	(7,050)
Loss on Sale of Equipment	(5,400)
Gain on Sale of Land	5,000
Income before Income Tax Expense	98,000
Income Tax Expense	29,400
Net Income (Loss)	$68,600

Notes:

The company paid cash dividends during 2019.
The company did not make a bonds payable payment during 2019.
The company did not purchase any equipment during 2019.
The company did not purchase any land during 2019.

Required

a)   Prepare the statement of cash flows for December 31, 2019 using the indirect method.

b) Prepare the statement of cash flows using the direct method. Assume accounts payable is only for the purchase of merchandise inventory. Do not show the reconciliation schedule of net income with net cash provided (used) by operating activities at the bottom of the statement of cash flows.

Analysis

a) Are there any concerns based on the statement of cash flows?

b) Are there any concerns in the cash flow from operating activities section?

AP-16A LO 2

2019 has been a great year for Exany Company, which managed to earn $56,000 of net income. Therefore, the board decided to declare and pay dividends by year end.

Based on the following information, answer the following questions.

Accounts	2019	2018
Retained Earnings	$91,000	$67,000
Common Stock	$120,000	$110,000

a) How much in dividends was paid in 2019?	
b) Which section of the statement of cash flows is affected?	
c) Assuming only the information given impacted the section of the statement of cash flows indicated in b), what is the net change in cash for this section?	

AP-17A LO 1 4

Cleancarpet Vacuums sells vacuum accessories. At the end of 2019, the statement of cash flows below was prepared.

Cleancarpet Vacuums Statement of Cash Flows For the Year Ended December 31, 2019		
Cash Flow from Operating Activities		
Net Income	$83,800	
Adjustments to Reconcile Net Income to Net Cash		
Provided (Used) by Operating Activities		
Depreciation Expense	4,760	
Gain on Sale of Equipment	(7,200)	
Change in Operating Assets and Liabilities		
Decrease in Accounts Receivable	2,210	
Increase in Merchandise Inventory	(46,800)	
Increase in Accounts Payable	6,000	
Net Cash Provided (Used) by Operating Activities		$42,770
Cash Flow from Investing Activities		
Sale of Equipment	20,300	
Net Cash Provided (Used) by Investing Activities		20,300
Cash Flow from Financing Activities		
Payment of Notes Payable	(19,100)	
Payment of Cash Dividend	(23,700)	
Net Cash Provided (Used) by Financing Activities		(42,800)
Net Increase (Decrease) in Cash		20,270
Cash at the Beginning of the Year		68,300
Cash at the End of the Year		$88,570

Required

a)   How much of the company's cash is from day-to-day operations?

_____

_____

b)   Why does the company have positive cash flow from investing activities? Would such positive cash flow from investing activities be sustainable?

_____

_____

_____

_____

_____

_____

c)   Calculate Cleancarpet Vacuums' free cash flow in 2019.

_____

_____

Analysis

What could Cleancarpet Vacuums do if selling the equipment was not an action the company could take, yet it still wanted to have a positive net cash flow at the end of the year?

_____

_____

AP-18A LO 7

The balance sheet and income statement for Beyond Lights Company are presented below.

Beyond Lights Company Balance Sheet As at December 31		
	2019	2018
Assets		
Cash	$133,400	$75,000
Accounts Receivable	47,000	26,000
Merchandise Inventory	72,000	42,000
Total Current Assets	252,400	143,000
Land	90,000	100,000
Equipment	90,000	130,000
Accumulated Depreciation	(45,000)	(60,000)
Total Assets	$387,400	$313,000
Liabilities		
Current Liabilities		
Accounts Payable	$35,000	$65,000
Notes Payable, Current Portion	40,000	40,000
Total Current Liabilities	75,000	105,000
Notes Payable, Long-Term Portion	140,000	95,000
Total Liabilities	215,000	200,000
Stockholders' Equity		
Common Stock	85,000	75,000
Retained Earnings	87,400	38,000
Total Stockholders' Equity	172,400	113,000
Total Liabilities and Stockholders' Equity	$387,400	$313,000

Beyond Lights Company Income Statement For the Year Ended December 31, 2019	
Sales	$380,000
Cost of Goods Sold	247,000
Gross Profit	133,000
Operating Expenses	
Depreciation Expense	5,000
Other Operating Expenses	29,600
Total Operating Expenses	34,600
Income from Operations	98,400
Other Income and Expenses	
Loss on Sale of Equipment	(5,400)
Gain on Sale of Land	5,000
Income before Income Tax Expense	98,000
Income Tax Expense	29,400
Net Income (Loss)	$68,600

Notes: The company did not purchase any land or equipment during the year.

Prepare a statement of cash flows using a spreadsheet by means of the indirect method.

	Balance		Changes		Balance
	Dec 31, 2018		Debit	Credit	Dec 31, 2019

Beyond Lights Company
Spreadsheet for Statement of Cash Flows
For the Year Ended December 31

Application Questions Group B

AP-1B LO 1

Indicate which section each item in the table below would appear in a statement of cash flows using the indirect method. Also indicate whether the item would increase or decrease cash using the indirect method.

Item	Section	Effect on Cash
Loss on sale of equipment		
Decrease in accounts payable		
Increase in merchandise inventory		
Depreciation expense		
Gain on sale of investments		
Dividends paid		
Issued shares in the company		
Net income		
Decrease in notes payable		
Sold equipment		
Decrease accounts receivable		
Loss on redemption of bonds		

AP-2B LO 2

Bonus Company had the following amounts in its statement of cash flows for the year ended December 31, 2019.

Net decrease in cash from operating activities	$100,000
Net decrease in cash from investing activities	400,000
Net increase in cash from financing activities	350,000
Cash balance, January 1, 2019	600,000

Calculate the cash balance at December 31, 2019.

AP-3B LO 2

The net income for the year ended December 31, 2019 for Kersley Company was $73,000. Additional information is shown below.

Interest expense on borrowing	$8,000
Gain on redemption of bonds	10,000
Increase in accounts receivable	10,000
Decrease in prepaid expense	3,000
Decrease in accounts payable	4,000
Dividends paid to common stockholders	14,000

Calculate the net cash provided (used) by operating activities.

_____
_____
_____
_____
_____

AP-4B LO 2

Use the following information to prepare the operating activities section of a statement of cash flows for MNO Co. for 2019 using the indirect method.

Net income	$140,000
Increase in merchandise inventory	30,000
Increase in accounts payable	20,000
Depreciation expense	55,000
Increase in accounts receivable	18,000
Gain on sale of land	25,000

_____
_____
_____
_____
_____
_____
_____

AP-5B LO 2

Danes Company had net income for 2019 of $120,000. Included in net income was a depreciation of $3,000, a gain on sale of land of $5,000, loss on redemption of bonds of $10,000 and income taxes of $30,000. Using the information given, calculate the net cash provided (used) by operating activities using the indirect method. Assume that the balances of current assets (except cash) and current liabilities remain the same as last year.

_____

_____

_____

_____

_____

Analysis

Why are some items from the income statement added back to net income on the statement of cash flows?

_____

_____

_____

_____

AP-6B LO 2

The following information pertains to Bush Company for the fiscal year 2019.

Purchase of plant and equipment	$33,000
Sale of long-term investments	12,000
Increase in accounts payable	6,000
Repayment of bonds payable	15,000
Depreciation of plant and equipment	7,000
Loss on redemption of bonds	5,000

Calculate the net cash provided (used) by investing activities.

_____

_____

_____

_____

AP-7B LO 2

The following events took place during 2019 at Bernard Company. Based on the information given, calculate net cash provided (used) by investing activities.

Gain on sale of investments	$4,000
Sale of investments (including gain)	50,000
Issued company stock	60,000
Paid off notes payable	30,000
Purchased equipment	70,000

_____

_____

_____

AP-8B LO 2

The following events took place during 2019 to Shaw Company. Based on the information given, calculate net cash provided (used) by financing activities.

Loss on sale of land	$10,000
Sale of land (including loss)	110,000
Issued company stock	120,000
Paid off notes payable	50,000
Paid dividends	30,000
Depreciation expense	6,000

_____

_____

_____

_____

_____

Analysis

If Shaw Company's net income during 2019 was $25,000, identify a potential concern from the cash flows from financing activities section.

_____

_____

_____

AP-9B LO 2

The following events took place during 2019 to Robinson Company. Based on the information given, calculate the net cash provided (used) by investing activities and financing activities.

Gain on sale of equipment	$2,000
Sale of equipment (including gain)	90,000
Purchase of long-term investments	65,000
Issued company stock	60,000
Issued a note payable	40,000
Paid dividends	20,000
Increase in merchandise inventory	24,000

Analysis

Suppose Robinson Company had a net increase in cash of $50,000. Explain why the company may be in trouble despite having a large increase in cash during the year.

AP-10B LO 3

Factsy Inc. is planning to make the best use out of its cash on hand by purchasing some additional long-term investments. Factsy's long-term investments are held at cost. In January 2019, Factsy bought additional investments. The company also sold part of its investments in November 2019 due to a sudden growth in the value of its holdings. December 31 is its year end.

Below are the data of Factsy Company.

Accounts	2019	2018
Long-Term Investment	$120,000	$110,000
Purchase of Investment	$40,000	
Gain on Sale of Investment	$5,000	

Calculate the net cash provided (used) by investing activities resulting from the long-term investment.

_____

_____

_____

_____

Analysis

Factsy's bookkeeper believes that the net change in cash from the investing activities must be a positive number (a cash inflow) as a result of a big gain on the sale of investment. Do you agree with this comment? Explain.

_____

_____

_____

_____

_____

_____

_____

_____

_____

_____

_____

_____

_____

_____

_____

_____

AP-11B LO 3

Flax Corporation's balance sheet accounts as at December 31, 2019 and 2018 are presented below.

Flax Corp. Balance Sheet As at December 31		
	2019	**2018**
Assets		
Current Assets		
Cash	$460,000	$300,000
Short-Term Investments	600,000	-
Accounts Receivable	1,020,000	1,020,000
Merchandise Inventory	1,360,000	1,200,000
Total Current Assets	3,440,000	2,520,000
Noncurrent Assets		
Long-Term Investments	400,000	800,000
Equipment	3,100,000	2,500,000
Accumulated Depreciation	(900,000)	(600,000)
Total Noncurrent Assets	2,600,000	2,700,000
Total Assets	$6,040,000	$5,220,000
Liabilities		
Current Liabilities	$2,300,000	$2,000,000
Long-Term Liabilities	800,000	700,000
Total Liabilities	3,100,000	2,700,000
Stockholders' Equity		
Common Stock	1,800,000	1,680,000
Retained Earnings	1,140,000	840,000
Total Stockholders' Equity	2,940,000	2,520,000
Total Liabilities and Stockholders' Equity	$6,040,000	$5,220,000

Assume current liabilities include only items from operations (e.g. accounts payable, taxes payable). Long-term liabilities include items from financing (e.g. bonds and other long-term liabilities).

Note that there was no sale of equipment throughout the year.

Prepare the statement of cash flows for 2019 using the indirect method. Assume the net income for 2019 was $300,000.

AP-12B LO 2 6

Vortex Manufacturing makes and sells integrated circuit boards. At the end of 2019, the income statement and comparative balance sheet were prepared as shown below.

Vortex Manufacturing **Balance Sheet** **As at December 31**		
	2019	**2018**
Assets		
Current Assets		
Cash	$239,820	$135,640
Accounts Receivable	242,100	265,300
Merchandise Inventory	503,200	465,300
Prepaid Expenses	26,500	26,500
Total Current Assets	1,011,620	892,740
Noncurrent Assets[1]		
Land	0	16,000
Equipment	840,400	840,400
Accumulated Depreciation	(102,300)	(95,600)
Total Noncurrent Assets	738,100	760,800
Total Assets	$1,749,720	$1,653,540
Liabilities		
Current Liabilities		
Accounts Payable	$305,600	$324,500
Notes Payable, Current Portion[2]	32,000	23,000
Total Current Liabilities	337,600	347,500
Notes Payable, Long-Term Portion[2]	205,000	185,000
Total Liabilities	542,600	532,500
Stockholders' Equity		
Common Stock	290,000	260,000
Retained Earnings	917,120	861,040
Total Stockholders' Equity	1,207,120	1,121,040
Total Liabilities and Stockholders' Equity	$1,749,720	$1,653,540

[1] During 2019, land was sold for a loss of $5,000. There was no purchase of equipment throughout the year.

[2] The company did not pay off any amount of the notes payable.

Vortex Manufacturing
Income Statement
For the Year Ended December 31, 2019

Sales	$2,650,000
Cost of Goods Sold	1,722,500
Gross Profit	927,500
Operating Expenses	
Depreciation Expense	6,700
Other Operating Expenses	752,600
Total Operating Expenses	759,300
Income from Operations	168,200
Other Income and Expenses	
Loss on Sale of Land	(5,000)
Income before Income Tax Expense	163,200
Income Tax Expense	57,120
Net Income (Loss)	$106,080

Required

a) Prepare the statement of cash flows using the indirect method.

b) Prepare the statement of cash flows using the direct method. Assume accounts payable is only for the purchase of merchandise inventory. Do not show the reconciliation schedule of net income with net cash provided (used) by operating activities at the bottom of the statement of cash flows.

AP-13B LO 2 3 6

The balance sheet and income statement for Venus Company are presented below.

Venus Company Balance Sheet As at December 31		
	2019	**2018**
Assets		
Cash	$191,410	$94,000
Accounts Receivable	30,000	34,000
Merchandise Inventory	42,000	50,000
Total Current Assets	263,410	178,000
Land	90,000	100,000
Building	125,000	130,000
Accumulated Depreciation	(62,000)	(60,000)
Total Assets	$416,410	$348,000
Liabilities		
Current Liabilities		
Accounts Payable	$76,000	$65,000
Notes Payable, Current Portion	45,000	40,000
Total Current Liabilities	121,000	105,000
Notes Payable, Long-Term Portion	120,000	95,000
Total Liabilities	241,000	200,000
Stockholders' Equity		
Common Stock	85,000	75,000
Retained Earnings	90,410	73,000
Total Stockholders' Equity	175,410	148,000
Total Liabilities and Stockholders' Equity	$416,410	$348,000

Venus Company Income Statement For the Year Ended December 31, 2019	
Sales	$380,000
Cost of Goods Sold	255,000
Gross Profit	125,000
Operating Expenses	
Depreciation Expense	42,000
Other Operating Expenses	28,500
Total Operating Expenses	70,500
Income from Operations	54,500
Other Income and Expenses	
Loss on Sale of Building	(5,400)
Gain on Sale of Land	3,200
Income before Income Tax Expense	52,300
Income Tax Expense	15,690
Net Income (Loss)	$36,610

Notes: Building and land were purchased for $115,000, and $200,000, respectively.
The company declared and paid dividends during the year.
The company did not pay off any amount of the notes payable.

Required

a)   Prepare the statement of cash flows for December 31, 2019 using the indirect method.

b) Prepare the statement of cash flows using the direct method. Assume accounts payable is only for the purchase of merchandise inventory. Do not show the reconciliation schedule of net income with net cash provided (used) by operating activities at the bottom of the statement of cash flows.

AP-14B LO 2 3 6

The balance sheet and income statement for Twely Inc. are presented below.

Twely Inc. Balance Sheet As at December 31		
	2019	**2018**
Assets		
Cash	$62,927	$56,000
Accounts Receivable	27,000	23,000
Merchandise Inventory	24,500	18,000
Total Current Assets	114,427	97,000
Long-Term Investment	42,000	45,000
Land	119,000	100,000
Equipment	89,000	76,000
Accumulated Depreciation	(28,200)	(24,000)
Total Assets	$336,227	$294,000
Liabilities		
Current Liabilities		
Accounts Payable	$29,000	$25,000
Notes Payable, Current Portion	22,000	22,000
Total Current Liabilities	51,000	47,000
Notes Payable, Long-Term Portion	79,000	65,000
Total Liabilities	130,000	112,000
Stockholders' Equity		
Common Stock	85,000	85,000
Retained Earnings	121,227	97,000
Total Stockholders' Equity	206,227	182,000
Total Liabilities and Stockholders' Equity	$336,227	$294,000

Twely Inc. Income Statement For the Year Ended December 31, 2019	
Sales	$140,000
Cost of Goods Sale	76,000
Gross Profit	64,000
Operating Expenses	
Depreciation Expense	8,200
Other Operating Expenses	14,790
Total Operating Expenses	22,990
Income from Operations	41,010
Other Income and Expenses	
Gain on Sale of Investment	1,100
Gain on Sale of Equipment	2,500
Income before Income Tax Expense	44,610
Income Tax Expense	13,383
Net Income (Loss)	$31,227

Notes: There was no sale of land.

Equipment and long-term investment were purchased for $30,000 and $10,500, respectively.

The long-term investment is held at cost.

The company declared and paid dividends during the year.

The company paid off $22,000 of the notes payable in 2019.

Required

a) Prepare the statement of cash flows for December 31, 2019 using the indirect method.

b)   Prepare the statement of cash flows using the direct method. Assume accounts payable is only for the purchase of merchandise inventory. Do not show the reconciliation schedule of net income with net cash provided (used) by operating activities at the bottom of the statement of cash flows.

AP-15B LO 2 3 6

The balance sheet and income statement for Joe's Fish Hut are presented below.

Joe's Fish Hut Balance Sheet As at December 31		
	2019	**2018**
Assets		
Cash	$2,100	$23,000
Accounts Receivable	21,000	12,000
Merchandise Inventory	21,000	25,000
Total Current Assets	44,100	60,000
Land	100,000	100,000
Equipment	170,000	150,000
Accumulated Depreciation	(28,600)	(25,000)
Total Assets	$285,500	$285,000
Liabilities		
Current Liabilities		
Accounts Payable	$23,000	$33,000
Notes Payable, Current Portion	12,000	12,000
Total Current Liabilities	35,000	45,000
Notes Payable, Long-Term Portion	48,000	60,000
Total Liabilities	83,000	105,000
Stockholders' Equity		
Paid-In Capital		
Preferred Shares	4,000	0
Common Shares	15,000	15,000
Additional Paid-In Capital	1,000	0
Total Paid-In Capital	20,000	15,000
Retained Earnings	182,500	165,000
Total Stockholders' Equity	202,500	180,000
Total Liabilities and Stockholders' Equity	$285,500	$285,000

Joe's Fish Hut Income Statement For the Year Ended December 31, 2019	
Sales	$161,000
Cost of Goods Sold	112,700
Gross Profit	48,300
Operating Expenses	
Depreciation Expense	3,600
Other Operating Expenses	19,700
Total Operating Expenses	23,300
Income before Income Tax Expense	25,000
Income Tax Expense	7,500
Net Income (Loss)	$17,500

Note:

The company did not sell any equipment during the year. The company did not sign any additional notes payable in 2019.

Required

a)   Prepare the statement of cash flows for December 31, 2019 using the indirect method.

b) Prepare the statement of cash flows using the direct method. Assume accounts payable is only for the purchase of merchandise inventory. Do not show the reconciliation schedule of net income with net cash provided (used) by operating activities at the bottom of the statement of cash flows.

Analysis

a) Are there any concerns based on the statement of cash flows?

_____

_____

_____

_____

b) Are there any concerns in the cash flow from the operating activities section?

_____

_____

_____

_____

AP-16B LO 1 2

Carlin Corporation has prepared the following statement of cash flows for the year end.

Carlin Corporation Statement of Cash Flows For the Year Ended December 31, 2019		
Cash Flow from Operating Activities		
Net Income	$56,200	
Adjustments to Reconcile Net Income to Net Cash		
Provided (Used) by Operating Activities		
Depreciation Expense	3,100	
Changes in Opening Assets and Liabilities		
Increase in Accounts Receivable	(31,000)	
Increase in Merchandise Inventory	(33,000)	
Decrease in Accounts Payable	(26,000)	
Net Cash Provided (Used) by Operating Activities		($30,700)
Cash Flow from Investing Activities		
Purchase of Equipment	(95,000)	
Sale of Land	120,000	
Net Cash Provided (Used) by Investing Activities		25,000
Cash Flow from Financing Activities		
Proceeds from Issuance of Common Stock	10,000	
Proceeds from Notes Payable	45,000	
Dividends Paid	(40,000)	
Net Cash Provided (Used) by Financing Activities		15,000
Net Increase (Decrease) in Cash		9,300
Cash at the Beginning of the Year		12,000
Cash at the End of the Year		$21,300

Required

a) The company had a net income during the year; however, they had a negative cash flow from operations. Identify the problems that led to a negative cash flow from operations.

_____

_____

_____

_____

b) Even though cash flow from operations was negative, total cash increased by $9,300. How did cash increase?

_____

_____

_____

c) Are there any other concerns regarding the statement of cash flows that have not been covered in parts a) and b)?

_____

_____

_____

AP-17B LO 1 2

Dawson Corporation has prepared the following statement of cash flows for the year end.

Dawson Corporation Statement of Cash Flows For the Year Ended December 31, 2019		
Cash Flow from Operating Activities		
Net Income	$68,000	
Adjustments to Reconcile Net Income to Net Cash		
Provided (Used) by Operating Activities		
Depreciation Expense	3,700	
Gain on Sale of Equipment	(8,000)	
Changes in Operating Assets and Liabilities		
Decrease in Accounts Receivable	15,000	
Increase in Merchandise Inventory	(60,000)	
Decrease in Accounts Payable	(5,000)	
Net Cash Provided (Used) by Operating Activities		$13,700
Cash Flow from Investing Activities		
Sale of Equipment	84,000	
Purchase of Land	(240,000)	
Net Cash Provided (Used) by Investing Activities		(156,000)
Cash Flow from Financing Activities		
Proceeds from Issuance of Common Stock	30,000	
Proceeds from Notes Payable	120,000	
Payment of Dividends	(10,000)	
Net Cash Provided (Used) by Financing Activities		140,000
Net Increase (Decrease) in Cash		(2,300)
Cash at the Beginning of the Year		12,000
Cash at the End of the year		$9,700

Required

a) The company had a total decrease in cash during the year of $2,300. What is the primary cause of this decrease in cash?

_____

_____

_____

b) Are there any concerns with operating activities?

_____

_____

Analysis

In a cash flow budgeting meeting, the company's CEO argued that, "we could have taken a larger loan to finance our land purchase in 2019. In fact, instead of borrowing only $120,000, we should have asked for $240,000. That would have put us into a better cash flow situation." Evaluate this comment from the CEO. How would a larger loan affect the cash flow of Dawson Corporation?

_____

_____

_____

_____

_____

_____

_____

_____

_____

_____

AP-18B LO 7

The balance sheet and income statement for Joe's Fish Hut are presented below.

Joe's Fish Hut
Balance Sheet
As at December 31

	2019	2018
Assets		
Cash	$2,100	$23,000
Accounts Receivable	21,000	12,000
Merchandise Inventory	21,000	25,000
Total Current Assets	44,100	60,000
Land	100,000	100,000
Equipment	170,000	150,000
Accumulated Depreciation	(28,600)	(25,000)
Total Assets	$285,500	$285,000
Liabilities		
Current Liabilities		
Accounts Payable	$23,000	$33,000
Notes Payable, Current Portion	12,000	12,000
Total Current Liabilities	35,000	45,000
Notes Payable, Long-Term Portion	48,000	60,000
Total Liabilities	83,000	105,000
Stockholders' Equity		
Paid-In Capital		
Preferred Stock	4,000	0
Common Stock	15,000	15,000
Additional Paid-In Capital	1,000	0
Total Paid-In Capital	20,000	15,000
Retained Earnings	182,500	165,000
Total Stockholders' Equity	202,500	180,000
Total Liabilities and Stockholders' Equity	$285,500	$285,000

Joe's Fish Hut
Income Statement
For the Year Ended December 31, 2019

Sales	$161,000
Cost of Goods Sold	112,700
Gross Profit	48,300
Operating Expenses	
Depreciation Expense	3,600
Other Operating Expenses	19,700
Total Operating Expenses	23,300
Income before Income Tax Expense	25,000
Income Tax Expense	7,500
Net Income (Loss)	$17,500

Notes:

The company did not sell any equipment during the year. The company did not sign any additional note payable in 2019.

Prepare a statement of cash flows using a work sheet (spreadsheet) by means of the indirect method.

	Balance	Changes		Balance
Joe's Fish Hut				
Work Sheet (Spreadsheet) for Statement of Cash Flows				
For the Year Ended December 31				
	Balance	**Changes**		**Balance**
	Dec 31, 2018	**Debit**	**Credit**	**Dec 31, 2019**

Case Study

Granite Surfaces specializes in making granite countertops. A new accounting clerk has compiled the following information to prepare the statement of cash flows for the year ended December 31, 2019.

- Net income for the year was $114,140.
- Depreciation expense was $15,300.
- Equipment was sold for a gain of $16,000. Cash proceeds from the sale were $36,000.
- Equipment was purchased for $250,000.
- Dividends of $50,000 were paid.
- Accounts receivable increased by $31,400.
- Merchandise inventory decreased by $38,700.
- Accounts payable increased by $41,100.
- Notes payable increased by $55,000.
- Stock was sold for $50,000 (also its book value).
- Cash balance on January 1, 2019 was $114,800.
- Cash balance on December 31, 2019 was $117,640.

The statement of cash flows the accounting clerk prepared is shown below.

Granite Surfaces Statement of Cash Flows For the Year Ended December 31, 2019		
Cash Flow from Operating Activities		
Net Income	$114,140	
Adjustments to Reconcile Net Income to Net Cash		
Provided (Used) by Operating Activities		
Depreciation Expense	15,300	
Changes in Operating Assets and Liabilities		
Increase in Accounts Receivable	31,400	
Decrease in Merchandise Inventory	(38,700)	
Increase in Accounts Payable	41,100	
Sale of Equipment	36,000	
Purchase of Equipment	(250,000)	
Net Cash Provided (Used) by Operating Activities		($50,760)
Cash Flow from Investing Activities		
Proceeds from Notes Payable	55,000	
Net Cash Provided (Used) by Investing Activities		55,000
Cash Flow from Financing Activities		
Payment of Cash Dividend	(50,000)	
Proceeds from Issuance of Common Stock	50,000	
Net Cash Provided (Used) by Financing Activities		0
Net Increase (Decrease) in Cash		4,240
Cash at the Beginning of the Year		114,800
Cash at the End of the Year		$119,040

Required

a)   Identify the problems with the statement of cash flows that the accounting clerk prepared.

_____

_____

_____

_____

_____

_____

b)   Prepare a corrected statement of cash flows.

Chapter 14

FINANCIAL STATEMENT ANALYSIS

LEARNING OBJECTIVES

LO **1** Explain the importance of analyzing financial statements

LO **2** Conduct a horizontal and vertical analysis of financial statements

LO **3** Calculate and apply liquidity ratios

LO **4** Calculate and apply profitability ratios

LO **5** Calculate and apply operations management and solvency ratios

LO **6** Calculate and apply capital market ratios

LO **7** Identify the limitations of financial statement analysis

AMEENGAGE *Access **ameengage.com** for integrated resources including tutorials, practice exercises, the digital textbook and more.*

Assessment Questions

AS-1 LO 1

What is financial analysis?

_____

_____

AS-2 LO 1

What is the Management's Discussion and Analysis (MD&A) section in a company's annual report?

_____

_____

AS-3 LO 4

What is the formula for gross profit margin?

_____

_____

AS-4 LO 4

What does gross profit margin tell us?

_____

_____

_____

AS-5 LO 5

What is the formula for the times interest earned ratio?

_____

_____

AS-6 LO 5

Is it more preferable to have a higher or lower interest coverage ratio? Explain.

_____

_____

AS-7 LO 4

How do you calculate net profit margin?

_____

_____

AS-8 LO 4

What is the formula for return on equity?

_____

_____

AS-9 LO 4

For a particular company, if net income increased significantly from one year to the next, does this guarantee that the return on equity will also increase? Explain.

_____

_____

_____

AS-10 LO 4

What is the formula for return on assets?

_____

_____

AS-11 LO 4

What are some possible reasons why return on assets may have decreased from one period to the next?

_____

_____

AS-12 `LO 4`

Suppose that Company A and Company B generate the same level of net income each period. However, Company A is more capital-intensive than Company B. Which company will likely have the higher return on assets?

_____

_____

_____

AS-13 `LO 3`

What is the formula for the current ratio?

_____

_____

AS-14 `LO 3`

What does the current ratio tell you?

_____

_____

AS-15 `LO 3`

If current assets stay constant from one period to the next, but current liabilities increase, what will happen to the current ratio?

_____

_____

AS-16 `LO 3`

What is the formula for the quick ratio?

_____

_____

AS-17 `LO 5`

What is the formula for the debt-to-equity ratio?

_____

_____

AS-18 `LO 5`

What is the formula for days' sales outstanding?

_____

_____

AS-19 LO 5

What does days' sales outstanding tell you?

_____

_____

AS-20 LO 5

How do you calculate accounts receivable turnover?

_____

_____

AS-21 LO 5

How is days' sales in inventory calculated?

_____

_____

AS-22 LO 5

What is the formula for the inventory turnover ratio?

_____

_____

AS-23 LO 7

Why is it necessary to compare a company's calculated ratios with industry benchmarks?

_____

_____

_____

_____

AS-24 LO 6

How is book value per common share calculated?

_____

_____

AS-25 LO 6

What does book value per common share tell us?

_____

_____

_____

_____

_____

AS-26 LO 6

How is earnings per share calculated? And what does it tell us?

_____

_____

_____

AS-27 LO 2

How does the base-year differ from the base-figure?

_____

_____

_____

_____

_____

_____

Application Questions Group A

AP-1A `LO` `4`

Simply Mullet Company reported the following.

- Sales: $1,000,000
- Cost of Goods Sold: $700,000
- Operating Expenses: $400,000
- Income Tax Rate: 20%

Calculate the gross profit margin. Differentiate between gross profit margin and gross profit.

_____

_____

_____

_____

_____

_____

_____

AP-2A `LO` `4` `5`

Trooper Nova Company reported the following.

Sales	$2,000,000
Cost of Goods Sold	700,000
Operating Expenses	400,000
Interest Expense included in Operating Expenses	50,000
Income Taxes	40% of income before tax
Stockholders' Equity (Average)	$20,000,000

Required
a)   Calculate net income.

_____

_____

_____

_____

b)   Calculate the net profit margin.

_____

_____

_____

c)   Calculate the times interest earned

_____

_____

_____

d) Calculate the return on equity. Banks are currently paying interest of 4% on deposits invested for two or more years. Comment on the ratio.

_____

_____

_____

_____

_____

AP-3A LO 3

All-You-Can-Buy Company reports current assets of $6,572, and current liabilities of $2,786. Calculate the current ratio and the working capital.

_____

_____

_____

AP-4A LO 3

Total current liabilities for Nicholson Restoration Company are $2,786. If cash is $2,000, short-term investments are $3,000, long-term investments are $1,000 and accounts receivable is $1,200, calculate the quick ratio.

_____

_____

AP-5A LO 4

The income statement of Ellen Corporation for the years 2018 and 2019 showed the following gross profit.

	2019	2018
Net Sales	$97,200	$80,000
Cost of Goods Sold	72,000	50,000
Gross Profit	$25,200	$30,000

Required

a) Calculate the gross profit margins for both years.

_____

_____

_____

_____

_____

_____

_____

b) In which year does Ellen Corporation have a better gross profit margin? Explain.

_____

_____

_____

_____

_____

AP-6A LO 5

Kingston Company sells on credit, with the balance due in 30 days. The company's DSO ratio has changed from 60 days last year to 42 days this year. Are things getting better or worse? Explain the relationship between the sales terms and DSO.

_____

_____

_____

_____

AP-7A LO 4 5

Presented below is the comparative income statement of Newton Company for 2019 and 2018.

Newton Company Income Statement For the Year Ended December 31		
	2019	**2018**
Sales	$194,890	$108,345
Cost of Goods Sold	116,934	65,007
Gross Profit	77,956	43,338
Operating Expenses		
Administrative Expense	12,000	8,000
Selling Expense Expense	22,540	13,627
Total Operating Expenses	34,540	21,627
Other Income and Expenses		
Interest Expense	1,248	580
Income before Income Tax Expense	42,168	21,131
Income Tax Expense	12,650	6,339
Net Income	**$29,518**	**$14,792**

Required

a) Calculate the following ratios for both years.

	2019	**2018**
Net Profit Margin		
Times Interest Earned Ratio		

b) In which year does the company have a better performance with respect to the ratios calculated in part a)? Explain.

_____

_____

_____

_____

AP-8A LO 5

At the beginning of 2019, Acatela Corp. had inventory of $350,000. During the year, it purchased $220,000 worth of raw materials and sold $500,000 worth of inventory. Determine the inventory turnover ratio and the days' sales in inventory.

_____

_____

_____

_____

_____

_____

_____

_____

AP-9A LO 5

At the end of 2019, accounts receivable amounted to $200,000. At the beginning of the year, it was $165,000. Net credit sales for the year amounted to $813,000 and net income was calculated to be $229,000.

Determine the days' sales outstanding ratio and the accounts receivable turnover ratio. Comment on the ability of the company to enforce its credit policy of 60 days.

_____

_____

_____

_____

AP-10A LO 3

Selected financial data from Crew Company is provided below.

	As at December 31, 2019
Cash	$75,000
Accounts Receivable	$225,000
Merchandise Inventory	$270,000
Short-Term Investments	$40,000
Land and Building	$500,000
Current Portion of Long-Term Debt	$30,000
Accounts Payable	$120,000

Required

a)   Calculate the quick ratio.

_____

_____

_____

_____

_____

_____

b)   What does Crew Company's quick ratio suggest about the company's performance?

_____

_____

AP-11A LO 5

Bo Kyung Company had a debt-to-equity ratio last year of 1.46. This year, the ratio is 2.0. Are things getting better or worse? Explain your answer.

_____

_____

_____

AP-12A LO 4 5

Presented below are select figures from the balance sheet of Edison Company for 2019 and 2018.

Edison Company Balance Sheet As at August 31		
	2019	**2018**
Total Assets	$286,633	$203,311
Total Liabilities	119,006	69,873
Stockholders' Equity	167,627	133,438

In 2019, Edison Company had sales of $413,000 and net income of $46,500. Calculate the ratios for 2019 as indicated below.

Return on Assets _____

Asset Turnover _____

Debt-to-Equity _____

Debt-to-Total-Assets _____

AP-13A LO 6

Testa Inc. had a net income of $158,000 for the year ended December 31, 2019. The company does not have any preferred stock and has 45,000 common shares outstanding for the entire year. During the year, they paid out $20,000 in dividends. Assume the market price of each common share is $24, which happens to be double of the book value per share.

Required

a) Calculate earnings per share.

_____

_____

_____

_____

b) Calculate the dividend yield.

_____

_____

_____

_____

c) Calculate the price-earnings ratio.

_____

_____

_____

_____

_____

AP-14A LO 6

Freebird Inc. had a net income of $358,400 for the year ended September 30, 2019. The company does not have any preferred stock and has 113,000 common shares outstanding for the entire year. During the year, they paid out $60,000 in dividends. Stockholders' equity is valued at $332,000. Assume the market price of each common share at the company's year end is $17 per share.

Required

a) Calculate earnings per share.

_____

_____

_____

b) Calculate the dividend yield.

_____

_____

c) Calculate the price-earnings ratio.

_____

_____

d) Calculate the book value per common share.

_____

_____

Analysis

Book value per common share is rarely equal to the selling price of the share on the stock market. What are some factors that could cause the market value to differ from the book value?

_____

_____

_____

_____

_____

_____

_____

_____

AP-15A LO 4

Below is select financial statement information for Rock Co. and Roll Inc.

	Rock Co.	Roll Inc.
Income Statement		
Sales	$348,500	$465,800
Cost of Goods Sold	106,293	160,701
Gross Profit	242,208	305,099
Expenses		
Salaries Expense	52,275	69,870
Depreciation Expense	34,850	46,580
Advertising Expense	17,425	23,290
Interest Expense	15,683	37,264
Total Expenses	120,233	177,004
Income before Income Tax Expense	121,975	128,095
Income Tax Expense	62,730	83,844
Net Income	$59,245	$44,251
Balance Sheet		
Cash	$14,850	$19,800
Accounts Receivable	25,000	22,500
Merchandise Inventory	34,500	43,125
Equipment	85,800	81,510
Total Assets	$160,150	$166,935
Accounts Payable	$27,500	$24,750
Unearned Revenue	17,800	19,580
Long-Term Liabilities	29,350	62,925
Stockholders' Equity	85,500	59,680
Total Liabilities and Stockholders' Equity	$160,150	$166,935

Required

a) Calculate the profitability ratios shown in the table below. For any ratios that require an average value from the balance sheet accounts, just use the single figure provided for each company.

	Rock Co.	Roll Inc.
Gross Profit Margin		
Net Profit Margin		
Return on Equity (ROE)		
Return on Assets (ROA)		

b) Based on the ratios from part a), which company would an investor be more likely to invest in?

_____

_____

_____

_____

AP-16A LO 3 4 5

Chicken Inc. and Egg Inc. are both in the toy retail business. All sales are on credit. Below is select financial information for the current year.

	Chicken Inc.	Egg Inc.
Income Statement		
Sales	$150,000	$135,000
Cost of Goods Sold	48,750	41,850
Gross Profit	101,250	93,150
Expenses		
Salaries Expense	22,500	27,000
Depreciation Expense	15,000	13,500
Advertising Expense	7,500	6,750
Interest Expense	6,750	5,130
Total Expenses	51,750	52,380
Income before Income Tax Expense	49,500	40,770
Income Tax Expense	26,250	24,300
Net Income	$23,250	$16,470
Balance Sheet		
Cash	$40,850	$24,510
Accounts Receivable	15,000	9,000
Merchandise Inventory	34,500	20,125
Equipment	85,800	51,480
Total Assets	$176,150	$105,115
Accounts Payable	21,000	32,000
Unearned Revenue	27,800	18,670
Long-Term Liabilities	39,350	15,635
Stockholders' Equity	88,000	38,810
Total Liabilities and Stockholders' Equity	$176,150	$105,115

Required

a) Calculate each ratio listed below for each company and indicate which company is better for each one. For any ratios that require an average value from the balance sheet accounts, just use the single figure provided for each company.

	Chicken Inc.	Egg Inc.	Which company is better?
Gross Profit Margin			
Net Profit Margin			
Return on Equity (ROE)			
Return on Assets (ROA)			
Asset Turnover			
Current Ratio			
Quick Ratio			
Debt-to-Equity Ratio			
Debt-to-Total-Assets Ratio			
Days' Sales Outstanding			
Accounts Receivable Turnover			
Days' Sales in Inventory			
Inventory Turnover			

b) Examining all of the ratios, explain which company has a stronger financial position in regards to the following categories.

   i. Profitability

_____

_____

_____

_____

_____

  ii. Liquidity

_____

_____

_____

 iii. Managerial performance

_____

_____

_____

_____

 iv. Solvency

_____

_____

_____

_____

AP-17A LO 3 4 5

The bookkeeper for Contigo Corporation has calculated several ratios for the past three fiscal years, shown below.

Required

a) For each of the ratios, indicate whether the ratio is improving or weakening overall from the previous years.

Contigo Corporation				
Ratio	2019	2018	2017	Improving or Weakening?
Gross Profit Margin	32.80%	31.50%	31.10%	
Return on Common Stockholders' Equity	18.04%	17.33%	17.11%	
Times Interest Earned Ratio	11.60	12.10	12.20	
Current Ratio	1.50	1.31	0.97	
Quick Ratio	0.90	0.79	0.73	
Debt-to-Equity Ratio	0.53	0.61	0.86	
Days' Sales Oustanding	31.50	31.20	30.80	
Days' Sales in Inventory	78.10	76.54	73.41	

b) Contigo is looking at applying for a new bank loan. The bank will examine the ratios that focus on the strength of Contigo's cash flow to determine if they should approve the loan. Based on the information in part a), would you recommend the bank to approve the bank loan? Why or why not?

_____

_____

_____

_____

_____

AP-18A LO 2

Perform a horizontal analysis for Groff Inc. Use 2016 as the base year and comment on the results.

Groff Inc. In Millions of Dollars				
	2019	2018	2017	2016
Sales Revenue	500	400	300	200
Net Income	166	158	144	120

Groff Inc. In Millions of Dollars				
	2019	2018	2017	2016
Sales Revenue				
Revenue Ratio				
Net Income				
Net Income Ratio				

_____

_____

_____

AP-19A LO 2

The following financial statements are taken from the records of Abaya Inc.

Abaya Inc. Balance Sheet As at December 31			
	2019	**2018**	**2017**
Current Assets			
Cash	$315,000	$325,000	$210,000
Accounts Receivable	140,000	198,000	92,000
Merchandise Inventory	411,000	397,000	428,000
Short-Term Investments	115,000	100,000	100,000
Total Current Assets	981,000	1,020,000	830,000
Noncurrent Assets	356,000	250,000	403,000
Total Assets	$1,337,000	$1,270,000	$1,233,000
Current Liabilities	214,000	265,000	90,000
Long-Term Liabilities	22,000	150,000	100,000
Total Liabilities	236,000	415,000	190,000
Stockholders' Equity	1,101,000	855,000	1,043,000
Total Liabilities and Stockholders' Equity	$1,337,000	$1,270,000	$1,233,000

Abaya Inc. Income Statement For the Year Ended December 31			
	2019	**2018**	**2017**
Sales	$701,000	$689,000	$514,000
Cost of Goods Sold	379,000	396,000	385,000
Gross Profit	322,000	293,000	129,000
Operating Expenses			
Administrative Expense	28,050	15,780	16,100
Selling Expense	65,000	34,000	30,000
Total Operating Expenses	93,050	49,780	46,100
Other Income and Expenses			
Interest Expense	18,600	12,600	8,500
Income before Income Tax Expense	210,350	230,620	74,400
Income Tax Expense	63,105	69,186	22,320
Net Income	$147,245	$161,434	$52,080

Required

a) Use horizontal analysis techniques to compare the changes between the 2019 and 2018 balance sheet items.

Abaya Inc. Balance Sheet As at December 31				
	2019	**2018**	**$ Change**	**% Change**
Current Assets				
Cash	$315,000	$325,000		
Accounts Receivable	140,000	198,000		
Merchandise Inventory	411,000	397,000		
Short-Term Investments	115,000	100,000		
Total Current Assets	981,000	1,020,000		
Noncurrent Assets	356,000	250,000		
Total Assets	$1,337,000	$1,270,000		
Current Liabilities	214,000	265,000		
Long-Term Liabilities	22,000	150,000		
Total Liabilities	236,000	415,000		
Stockholders' Equity	1,101,000	855,000		
Total Liabilities and Stockholders' Equity	$1,337,000	$1,270,000		

b) Using 2017 as a base year, provide a horizontal analysis of sales, gross profit, operating expenses and net income.

	2019	**2018**	**2017**
Sales			
Gross Profit			
Operating Expenses			
Net Income			

c) Perform a vertical analysis of income statement for 2019, 2018 and 2017 and state all of the income statement items as a percentage of net sales.

Abaya Inc. Income Statement For the Year Ended December 31			
	2019	**2018**	**2017**
Sales			
Cost of Goods Sold			
Gross Profit			
Operating Expenses			
Administrative Expense			
Selling Expense			
Total Operating Expenses			
Other Income and Expenses			
Interest Expense			
Income before Income Tax Expense			
Income Tax Expense			
Net Income			

_____

_____

_____

_____

_____

AP-20A LO 2

Perform a vertical analysis (use Sales as the base) for Hiltonia Inc. Comment on the results. Note that figures are in millions of dollars.

	Hiltonia Inc.	
	2019	**2018**
Sales	$210	$250
COGS	150	200
Gross Profit	60	50
Selling Expenses	5	4
Salaries	2	2
Rent	5	5
Total Expenses	12	11
Income before Tax	48	39
Taxes (35%)	16.8	13.65
Net Income	$31.2	$25.35

	Hiltonia Inc.			
	2019	**% of Sales**	**2018**	**% of Sales**
Sales				
COGS				
Gross Profit				
Selling Expenses				
Salaries				
Rent				
Total Expenses				
Income before Tax				
Taxes (35%)				
Net Income				

AP-21A LO 3 4 5 6

The income statements and balance sheets for Fallon Inc. are shown below for the last three fiscal years.

Fallon Inc. Income Statement For the Year Ended			
	2019	**2018**	**2017**
Sales	$360,000	$324,000	$342,000
Cost of Goods Sold	108,000	89,100	85,500
Gross Profit	252,000	234,900	256,500
Expenses			
Operating Expense	54,000	48,600	51,300
Depreciation Expense	36,000	32,400	34,200
Advertising Expense	18,000	16,200	17,100
Interest Expense	6,800	7,650	8,500
Total Expenses	114,800	104,850	111,100
Income before Income Tax Expense	137,200	130,050	145,400
Income Tax Expense	72,000	64,800	68,400
Net Income	$65,200	$65,250	$77,000

Fallon Inc. Balance Sheet At the Year Ended			
	2019	**2018**	**2017**
Cash	$63,650	$39,750	$36,000
Short-Term Investments	11,000	10,000	8,000
Accounts Receivable	48,000	40,000	32,000
Merchandise Inventory	18,000	22,500	27,000
Equipment	110,000	104,500	83,600
Total Assets	$250,650	$216,750	$186,600
Accounts Payable	$52,800	$44,000	$35,200
Current Portion of Long-Term Debt	8,500	8,500	8,500
Long-Term Debt	68,000	76,500	85,000
Common Stock	66,000	57,600	57,000
Retained Earnings	55,350	30,150	900
Total Liabilities and Stockholders' Equity	$250,650	$216,750	$186,600

Other Information

1) Fallon Inc. has an unlimited number of shares authorized. The following number of common shares were outstanding in each year for the entire year: 2019—50,000, 2018—48,000, 2017—47,000.

2) The following dividends were paid: $40,000 in 2019, $36,000 in 2018 and $38,000 in 2017.

Required

a) Calculate the following ratios for Fallon Inc. for 2018 and 2019, and state whether the ratio improved or weakened in 2019.

	2019	2018	Improved or Weakened
Gross Profit Margin			
Times Interest Earned Ratio			
Net Profit Margin			
Return on Equity (ROE)			
Return on Assets (ROA)			
Asset Turnover			
Current Ratio			
Quick Ratio			
Debt-to-Equity Ratio			
Debt-to-Total-Assets Ratio			
Days' Sales Outstanding			
Accounts Receivable Turnover			
Days' Sales in Inventory			
Inventory Turnover			
Book Value per Common Share			
Earnings per Share			

b) Fallon Inc. has a credit policy of 30 days. That is, it expects all customers to pay their bills within 30 days from sale. Comment on the company's ability to enforce this policy.

_____

_____

_____

_____

_____

Analysis

Comment on the company's ability to cover its short-term debt obligations.

_____

_____

_____

_____

_____

AP-22A LO 4

The stockholders' equity section of Adora Corporation's balance sheet as at December 31, 2018 and 2019 is presented below.

	2019	2018
Stockholders' Equity		
Paid-In Capital		
Preferred stock, $7, noncumulative, 10,000 shares authorized,		
1,000 shares issued and outstanding	$100,000	$100,000
Common stock, unlimited shares authorized,		
50,000 shares issued and outstanding	500,000	500,000
Total Paid-In Capital	600,000	600,000
Retained Earnings	338,000	300,000
Total Stockholders' Equity	938,000	900,000

Both preferred and common stock do not have par value. There were no changes in the number of shares of preferred and common stock during 2018 and 2019. Adora announced and paid preferred dividends of $7 per share and common dividends of $0.50 per share in 2019. Its net income in 2019 was $70,000.

Required

a) Calculate Adora's return on equity for 2019. Round your answer to two decimal places.

b) Calculate Adora's return on common stockholders' equity for the year 2019. Round your answer to two decimal places.

Application Questions Group B

AP-1B LO 4

Gross profit increased from $300,000 in 2018, to $400,000 in 2019. Gross profit margin decreased from 30% in 2018, to 28% in 2019. Comment on whether or not the company's profitability improved or deteriorated.

AP-2B LO 4 5

Sou Heng Company reported the following financial information at the end of 2019.

Sales Revenue	$2,110,000
Cost of Goods Sold	$740,000
Operating Expenses	$394,000
Interest Expense included in Operating Expenses	$53,000
Income Tax Expense	38% of income
Stockholders' Equity (Average)	$18,000,000

Required

a) Calculate net income.

b) Calculate the net profit margin.

c) Calculate the times interest earned.

d) Calculate the return on equity.

AP-3B [LO 3]

Goliath Gardening Services Ltd. reports current assets of $6,261, and current liabilities of $2,925. Calculate the current ratio and the working capital. Comment on the company's ability to cover short-term obligations.

_____

_____

_____

_____

AP-4B [LO 3]

Selected financial data from Jai Home Company is provided below.

Cash	$85,000
Accounts Receivable	$233,000
Merchandise Inventory	$267,000
Short-Term Investments	$50,000
Land and Building	$464,000
Current Portion of Long-Term Debt	$36,000
Accounts Payable	$117,000

Required

a) Calculate the quick ratio.

_____

_____

b) True or False? The quick ratio calculated in part a) shows that Jai Home Company is likely to meet its short-term cash obligations.

_____

_____

_____

AP-5B [LO 4]

The income statement for Ellen Corporation for the years 2018 and 2019 showed the following information.

	2019	2018
Sales Revenue	$98,000	$66,000
Cost of Goods Sold	$77,000	$43,000
Gross Profit	$21,000	$23,000

Required

a) Calculate the gross profit margins for both years.

_____

_____

b) In which year does Ellen Corporation have a better gross profit margin?

_____

_____

AP-6B LO 5

At the end of 2019, accounts receivable for Genuine Interiors amounted to $210,000. At the beginning of the year, it was $200,000. Net credit sales for the year amounted to $900,000 and net income was calculated to be $205,000.

Determine the days' sales outstanding ratio and the accounts receivable turnover ratio.

_____

_____

_____

Analysis

Generally, a lower days' sales outstanding (DSO) is desirable, since it means collections are happening faster for the company. Is there any drawback to getting the DSO extremely low, such as to only two or three days?

_____

_____

_____

_____

_____

AP-7B LO 4 5

Presented below is the comparative income statement of JeansWear Company for 2019 and 2018.

JeansWear Company Income Statement For the Year Ended January 31		
	2019	**2018**
Sales	$184,794	$107,933
Cost of Goods Sold	115,550	69,022
Gross Profit	69,244	38,911
Operating Expenses		
Administrative Expense	9,770	4,485
Selling Expense	22,000	16,000
Total Operating Expenses	31,770	20,485
Other Income and Expenses		
Interest Expense	1,343	579
Income before Income Tax Expense	36,131	17,847
Income Tax Expense	10,839	5,354
Net Income	$25,292	$12,493

Required

a) Calculate the following ratios for both years.

	2019	2018
Net Profit Margin		
Times Interest Earned Ratio		

b) In which year does the company have a better performance with respect to the net profit margin calculated in part a)?

_____

_____

AP-8B LO 5

At the beginning of 2019, Percolate Corp. had inventory of $337,000. During the year, it purchased $210,000 worth of raw materials and sold $505,000 worth of inventory. Determine the inventory turnover ratio and the days' sales in inventory. Comment on the company's ability to sell its inventory, which has a shelf-life of 90 days.

_____

_____

_____

_____

_____

AP-9B LO 5 7

Below is the past annual information for Java Time Inc. All sales are on credit.

	2019	2018	2017	2016
Sales	$44,500	$46,280	$47,900	$55,085
Sales Discounts	2,003	2,083	2,155	2,479
Net Sales	42,498	44,197	45,744	52,606
Accounts Receivable	6,130	5,885	5,649	5,084

Required

a) Calculate the following ratios for 2017, 2018 and 2019.

	2019	2018	2017
Days' Sales Outstanding			
Accounts Receivable Turnover			

b) Are the ratios improving or weakening? What could the company do to better control these ratios?

_____

_____

_____

_____

_____

AP-10B `LO 3`

Information from Silky Company's year-end financial statements is as follows.

	2019	2018
Current Assets	$200,000	$210,000
Current Liabilities	100,000	90,000
Stockholders' Equity	250,000	270,000
Net Sales	830,000	880,000
Cost of Goods Sold	620,000	640,000
Operating Income	50,000	55,000

Required

a) Calculate the current ratio for both years.

b) In which year does Silky Company have a better current ratio? Explain.

AP-11B `LO 4`

Selected information for the Universal Company is as follows.

	December 31		
	2019	2018	2017
Common Stock	$840,000	$648,000	$550,000
Retained Earnings	370,000	248,000	150,000
Net Income for the Year	240,000	122,000	98,000

Required

a) Calculate the return on equity ratio for 2019 and 2018.

b)   Has the Universal Company's performance improved in 2019? Explain using the return on equity ratio.

_____

_____

_____

AP-12B LO 5

Below is selected financial information for Swingline Inc.

	2019	2018	2017	2016
Ending Inventory	4,850	5,626	5,723	6,014
Cost of Goods Sold	68,950	72,398	65,503	71,708

Required

a)   Calculate the following ratios for 2019, 2018 and 2017.

	2019	2018	2017
Days' Sales in Inventory			
Inventory Turnover			

b)   Are the ratios improving or weakening? What could the company do to better control these ratios?

_____

_____

_____

_____

_____

AP-13B LO 6

Bluebird Inc. had a net income of $387,400 for the year ended August 31, 2019. The company does not have any preferred stock and has 125,000 shares of common stock outstanding for the entire year. During the year, they paid out $60,000 in dividends. Assume the market price of each common share at the company's year end is $12 per share.

Required

a)   Calculate earnings per share.

_____

_____

_____

_____

_____

b) Calculate the dividend yield.

_____

_____

_____

_____

_____

c) Calculate the price-earnings ratio.

_____

_____

_____

_____

_____

AP-14B LO 6

Below is select financial statement information for Beta Corp. and Gamma Inc. in 2019.

	Beta Corp.	Gamma Inc.
Net Income	$157,840	$246,850
Stockholders' Equity		
Preferred Stock	$8,740	$74,055
Common Stock	102,596	160,453
Retained Earnings	7,352	4,355
Total Stockholders' Equity	118,688	238,863
Number of Common Shares Outstanding	10,820	12,400

Both Beta and Gamma declared preferred dividends in 2019. For Beta, the total preferred dividends were equal to 5% of net income; for Gamma, they were equal to 8% of net income.

Required

a) Calculate the following ratios for each company.

	Beta Corp.	Gamma Inc.
Book Value per Common Share		
Earnings per Share (EPS)		

b) Based on the ratios from part a), which company would an investor be more likely to invest in?

_____

_____

_____

_____

AP-15B LO 3 4 5

Below is select financial statement information for Alpha Inc. and Delta Corp.

	Alpha Inc.	Delta Corp.
Income Statement		
Sales	$105,000	$87,000
Cost of Goods Sold	34,125	29,580
Gross Profit	70,875	57,420
Expenses		
Salaries Expense	15,750	13,050
Depreciation Expense	10,500	8,700
Advertising Expense	5,250	4,350
Interest Expense	8,925	4,524
Total Expenses	40,425	30,624
Income before Income Tax Expense	30,450	26,796
Income Tax Expense	18,900	15,660
Net Income	$11,550	$11,136
Balance Sheet		
Cash	$18,525	$24,700
Accounts Receivable	12,300	21,070
Merchandise Inventory	34,500	30,125
Equipment	66,800	63,460
Total Assets	$132,125	$139,355
Accounts Payable	$43,530	$33,177
Unearned Revenue	17,800	29,580
Current Portion of Long-Term Debt	8,304	1,324
Long-Term Debt	27,680	8,825
Stockholders' Equity	34,811	66,449
Total Liabilities and Stockholders' Equity	$132,125	$139,355

Required

a) Calculate the liquidity and solvency ratios as shown in the table below.

	Alpha Inc.	Delta Corp.
Debt-to-Total-Assets Ratio		
Times Interest Earned Ratio		
Current Ratio		
Quick Ratio		
Debt-to-Equity Ratio		

b) Which company has stronger liquidity and solvency ratios? Which company would a bank prefer to provide lending to based on the calculations in part a)?

_____

_____

_____

_____

_____

_____

_____

_____

_____

_____

_____

_____

_____

_____

AP-16B LO 7

The following information is available for three different companies within the same industry.

	Company A	Company B	Company C
Cash	$7,800	$7,020	$10,530
Short-Term Investments	2,000	1,800	4,700
Accounts Receivable	8,250	7,425	13,138
Prepaid Expenses	1,500	1,350	3,025
Merchandise Inventory	9,500	8,550	5,825
Total Current Assets	$29,050	$26,145	$37,218
Accounts Payable	$4,300	$4,515	$4,730
Deferred Revenue	7,500	7,875	8,250
Current Portion of Long-Term Debt	15,800	16,590	17,380
Total Current Liabilities	$27,600	$28,980	$30,360

Required

a) Calculate the current and quick ratios for each company listed below. Which company has the strongest and weakest liquidity?

	Company A	Company B	Company C
Current Ratio			
Quick Ratio			

b) Is the current ratio adequate for each company? Explain.

c) Is the quick ratio adequate for each company? Explain.

Analysis

All three companies are public companies and thus prepare their financial statements in accordance to GAAP. Does this mean that all values on their financial statements can be compared without further investigation into how the values were calculated?

AP-17B LO 3 4 5

The most recent income statements and balance sheets for Midland Company are shown below.

Midland Company Income Statement For the Year Ended		
	2019	**2018**
Sales (on Credit)	$600,000	$540,000
Cost of Goods Sold	252,000	216,000
Gross Profit	348,000	324,000
Expenses		
Salaries Expense	210,000	162,000
Depreciation Expense	48,000	54,000
Advertising Expense	60,000	54,000
Interest Expense	9,000	9,000
Total Expenses	327,000	279,000
Income before Income Tax Expense	21,000	45,000
Income Tax Expense	8,400	18,000
Net Income	$12,600	$27,000

Midland Company Balance Sheet At the Year Ended		
	2019	**2018**
Cash	$76,540	$41,400
Accounts Receivable	37,000	44,400
Merchandise Inventory	73,000	54,750
Equipment	110,000	158,000
Total Assets	$296,540	$298,550
Accounts Payable	$24,050	$28,860
Unearned Revenue	14,000	23,800
Long-Term Debt	60,000	60,000
Common Stock	50,000	50,000
Retained Earnings	148,490	135,890
Total Liabilities and Stockholders' Equity	$296,540	$298,550

Required

a) Calculate the following ratios for Midland Company for its 2019 fiscal year.

	Industry Average	Midland Company
Gross Profit Margin	40.0%	
Net Profit Margin	5.0%	
Return on Equity (ROE)	8.0%	
Return on Assets (ROA)	6.9%	
Quick Ratio	1.2	
Debt-to-Equity Ratio	0.75	
Days' Sales Outstanding	40.0	
Inventory Turnover	6.1	

b) Perform some ratio analysis to determine how Midland Company has performed in 2019 compared to the industry average.

_____

_____

_____

_____

_____

_____

_____

_____

AP-18B LO 2

Perform a horizontal analysis for Mazzic Inc. Use 2016 as the base year.

Mazzic Inc. In Millions of Dollars				
	2019	2018	2017	2016
Revenue	$469	$331	$292	$197
Revenue Percentage of 2016 Base-Year				
Net Income	$258	$223	$178	$84
Net Income Percentage of 2016 Base-Year				

AP-19B LO 2

The following financial statements are taken from the records of Jade Inc.

Required

a) Use horizontal analysis techniques to compare the changes between 2019 and 2018 balance sheet items.

Jade Inc. Balance Sheet As at October 31				
	2019	**2018**	**$ Change**	**% Change**
Current Assets				
Cash	$318,300	$319,400		
Accounts Receivable	150,900	170,100		
Merchandise Inventory	381,200	414,800		
Short-Term Investments	116,500	104,700		
Total Current Assets	966,900	1,009,000		
Noncurrent Assets	527,850	318,900		
Total Assets	$1,494,750	$1,327,900		
Current Liabilities	$258,200	$224,600		
Long-Term Liabilities	126,900	109,500		
Total Liabilities	385,100	334,100		
Stockholders' Equity	1,109,650	993,800		
Total Liabilities and Equity	$1,494,750	$1,327,900		

b) Perform a vertical analysis of the income statement for 2019 and state all the income statement items as a percentage of net sales.

Jade Inc. Income Statement For the Year Ended October 31		
	2019	**2019**
Sales	$700,800	
Cost of Goods Sold	373,800	
Gross Profit	327,000	
Expenses		
Advertising	4,400	
Utilities	8,200	
Rent	4,300	
Salaries and Wages	47,000	
Depreciation	34,530	
Interest	7,620	
Total Expenses	106,050	
Income before Income Tax Expense	220,950	
Income Tax Expense	55,100	
Net Income	$165,850	

Analysis

Analyze the strengths and weaknesses of Jade's financial position based on the above horizontal and vertical analyses.

_____

_____

_____

_____

_____

_____

_____

_____

_____

_____

_____

_____

_____

AP-20B LO 4 7

The financial information at December 31, 2019 for two similar companies is shown below.

	Shaken Inc.		Stirred Inc.	
Balance Sheet				
Average Total Assets		$80,000		$50,000
Average Stockholders' Equity		30,000		45,000
Income Statement				
Sales		100,000		68,000
Cost of Goods Sold		40,000		34,000
Gross Profit		60,000		34,000
Expenses				
Advertising Expense	$20,000		$5,000	
Salaries Expense	15,000		18,000	
Rent Expense	10,000		-	
Depreciation Expense	2,500		1,000	
Interest Expense	1,500		500	
Total Expenses		49,000		24,500
Net Income		$11,000		$9,500

Which company performed better during the year? Use relevant ratios to support your answer.

	Shaken Inc.	Stirred Inc.
Gross Profit Margin		
Net Profit Margin		
Asset Turnover		
Return on Equity		
Return on Assets		

_____

_____

_____

_____

Analysis

The comparison between these two companies assumes they are following the same accounting standards (GAAP or IFRS). What impact, if any, would there be on the comparison if one followed GAAP and the other followed IFRS?

AP-21B LO 3 4 5 6

The income statements and balance sheets for Hathaway Inc. are shown below for the last three fiscal years. All sales are on credit.

Hathaway Inc. Income Statement For the Year Ended			
	2019	**2018**	**2017**
Sales	$800,000	$720,000	$760,000
Cost of Goods Sold	260,000	288,000	266,000
Gross Profit	540,000	432,000	494,000
Expenses			
Operating Expense	320,000	216,000	342,000
Depreciation Expense	64,000	72,000	76,000
Advertising Expense	80,000	72,000	114,000
Interest Expense	10,000	10,000	10,000
Total Expenses	474,000	370,000	542,000
Income (Loss) before Income Tax Expense (Benefit)	66,000	62,000	(48,000)
Income Tax Expense Benefit	29,700	27,900	(21,600)
Net Income (Loss)	$36,300	$34,100	($26,400)

Hathaway Inc. Balance Sheet At the Year Ended			
	2019	**2018**	**2017**
Cash	$234,400	$149,600	$80,000
Accounts Receivable	84,000	70,000	56,000
Merchandise Inventory	136,000	102,000	61,200
Equipment	110,000	174,000	246,000
Total Assets	$564,400	$495,600	$443,200
Accounts Payable	$54,600	$45,500	$36,400
Unearned Revenue	21,000	23,100	18,900
Long-Term Debt	50,000	50,000	50,000
Common Stock	85,500	60,000	55,000
Retained Earnings	353,300	317,000	282,900
Total Liabilities and Stockholders' Equity	$564,400	$495,600	$443,200

Other Information

Hathaway Inc. has an unlimited number of shares authorized; the following common shares were outstanding in each year for the entire year: 2019—60,000, 2018—40,000, 2017—30,000.

Required

a) Calculate the following ratios for Hathaway Inc. for 2018 and 2019, and state whether the ratio improved or weakened in 2019.

	2019	**2018**	**Improved or Weakened**
Gross Profit Margin			
Times Interest Earned Ratio			
Net Profit Margin			
Return on Equity (ROE)			
Return on Assets (ROA)			
Current Ratio			
Quick Ratio			
Debt-to-Equity Ratio			
Debt-to-Total-Assets Ratio			
Days' Sales Outstanding			
Accounts Receivable Turnover			
Days' Sales in Inventory			
Inventory Turnover			
Book Value Per Common Share			
Earnings Per Share			

b) The owner of Hathaway Inc. is pleased to see that the company has started generating profits again and assumes that profitability must be improving. Perform some ratio analysis to determine if the owner's assumption is correct or not. Explain.

_____

_____

_____

_____

_____

Analysis

What does the company's inventory turnover ratio indicate/suggest?

_____

_____

_____

AP-22B `LO 4`

The following information is extracted from the financial statements of Knight Inc. and Emperor Corp.

	Knight	Emperor
Sales Revenue	$600,000	$400,000
Net Income	70,000	35,000
Average Total Assets	1,600,000	1,000,000
Average Total Liabilities	650,000	200,000
Average Total Stockholders' Equity	950,000	800,000
Average Preferred Stock	40,000	150,000
Total preferred dividends declared and paid during the year	3,200	9,000
Total common dividends declared and paid during the year	6,000	4,900

Required

a) Calculate net profit margin for both companies.

_____

_____

_____

b) Calculate return on equity for both companies.

_____

_____

_____

c) Calculate return on common stockholders' equity for both companies.

_____

_____

_____

_____

_____

_____

d) Calculate return on assets for both companies.

_____

_____

_____

_____

e) Based on all the ratios calculated in parts a) to d), which company's common stock is more attractive to potential investors?

_____

_____

_____

_____

_____

_____

_____

_____

_____

_____

Case Study

CS-1 LO 3 4 5

Suppose that you have decided to invest some money in the stock market. After some research online, you come across the financial statements of Yong Wireless Limited. Before you can make a decision to invest in the company, you will need to calculate some key financial ratios and then analyze them. The statements are presented below.

Yong Wireless Limited Consolidated Balance Sheet (in thousands) As at February 28		
	2019	**2018**
Assets		
Cash	$1,550,861	$835,546
Short-Term Investments	360,614	682,666
Accounts Receivable	2,800,115	2,269,845
Merchandise Inventory	621,611	682,400
Other Current Assets	479,455	371,129
Total Current Assets	5,812,656	4,841,586
Long-Term Investment	958,248	720,635
Property, Plant and Equipment	1,956,581	1,334,648
Intangible Assets	1,476,924	1,204,503
Total Assets	$10,204,409	$8,101,372
Liabilities		
Accounts Payable	$615,620	$448,339
Accrued Liabilities	1,638,260	1,238,602
Income Taxes Payable	95,650	361,460
Other Current Liabilities	82,247	66,950
Total Current Liabilities	2,431,777	2,115,351
Long-Term Liabilities	169,969	111,893
Total Liabilities	2,601,746	2,227,244
Stockholders' Equity		
Common Stock	2,113,146	2,208,235
Retained Earnings	5,489,517	3,665,893
Stockholders' Equity	7,602,663	5,874,128
Liabilities and Stockholders' Equity	$10,204,409	$8,101,372

Yong Wireless Limited Consolidated Income Statement (in thousands) For the Year Ended February 28		
	2019	**2018**
Revenue	$14,953,224	$11,065,186
Cost of Sales	8,368,958	5,967,888
Gross Profit	6,584,266	5,097,298
Operating Expenses		
Research and Development	964,841	684,702
Selling, Marketing and Admin	1,907,398	1,495,697
Amortization Expense	310,357	194,803
Litigation Expense	163,800	0
Total Operating Expenses	3,346,396	2,375,202
Income from Operations	3,237,870	2,722,096
Other Income and Expenses		
Investment Income	28,640	78,267
Income before Income Tax Expense	3,266,510	2,800,363
Income Tax Expense	809,366	907,747
Net Income	$2,457,144	$1,892,616

Yong Wireless Limited Summary of the Statement of Cash Flows (in thousands) For the Year Ended February 28		
	2019	**2018**
Net Cash Provided by Operations	$3,034,874	$1,451,845
Net Cash Used by Investing	($1,470,127)	($1,823,523)
Net Cash Used by Financing	($849,432)	$22,826
Net Increase (Decrease) in Cash	$715,315	($348,852)

Required

a) Calculate the following ratios for Yong Wireless Limited for 2019 and 2018. For any ratios that require an average (i.e. ROE), use the closing balance for the year.

	2019	2018
Gross Profit Margin		
Net Profit Margin		
Return on Equity		
Return on Assets		
Asset Turnover		
Current Ratio		
Quick Ratio		
Debt-to-Equity Ratio		

b) Based on the figures you calculated, has the company shown improvement in 2019 over 2018? Would you invest in Yong Wireless Limited? Explain.

_____

_____

_____

_____

_____

_____

_____

_____

_____

_____

CS-2 LO 3 4 5

The following information has been taken from the financial statements of Ivory Inc.

Ivory Inc.	
Current Assets, December 31, 2019	$175,000
Total Assets, January 1, 2019	500,000
Total Assets, December 31, 2019	575,000
Current Liabilities, December 31, 2019	75,000
Total Liabilities, December 31, 2019	175,000
Stockholders' Equity, January 1, 2019	300,000
Stockholders' Equity, December 31, 2019	400,000
Net Sales	900,000
Depreciation Expense	10,000
Interest Expense	20,000
Income Tax Expense	25,000
Net Income	40,000

Required

a) Given the data for Ivory Inc., calculate the following ratios for 2019 (round to two decimal places). The company's ratios for 2018 are given for comparison.

	Ratio	2018
i)	Current Ratio	3.5
ii)	Times Interest Earned Ratio	5.40
iii)	Debt-to-Equity	25.00%
iv)	Return on Assets	12.50%
v)	Return on Equity	20.20%
vi)	Net Profit Margin	8.60%

Ratio	2019

b) Using 2019 as a comparison, discuss whether the company improved or deteriorated in its ability to (i) pay current liabilities as they come due, (ii) meet its long-term debt obligations and (iii) profitability. Be sure to make reference to specific ratios in your answers.

_____

_____

_____

_____

_____

_____

_____

_____

_____

_____

_____

_____

_____

_____

_____

_____

_____

_____

_____

_____

_____

_____

_____

_____

Critical Thinking

CT-1 LO 7

Financial statement analysis is performed on historical information. Since the past cannot be changed, calculating financial ratios is of no use. What management and investors are really interested in is the future, specifically the future profitability of a company. Discuss.

_____

_____

_____

_____

_____

_____

_____

_____

_____

_____

_____

_____

_____

_____

_____

_____

_____

_____

_____

_____

_____

_____

_____

_____

_____

_____

_____

_____

_____

_____

_____